THE STRESS MAZE

By Andrea Ursula Hochgatterer

Published by The Book Chief Publishing House 2022

Suite 2A, Blackthorn House, St Paul's Square, Birmingham, B3 1RL

www.thebookchief.com

Book Cover Designer / Illustrator: Deearo Marketing

Editor: Laura Billingham

Typesetters: Elke Wallace / Sharon Brown

Illustration: Deearo Marketing

Publisher: Sharon Brown

THE BOOK CHIEF®

IGNITE YOUR WRITING

Table of Contents

Preface

Without understanding its meaning, my fascination with stress started very early on in life. I remember my childhood, watching and listening to confusing and scary events unfolding around me. Seeing adults' irrational reactions and behaviour, and constantly wondering why - why would people be kind and nice one minute and next, all storms would break loose? It was explained to me that this was "just stress", and it would blow over.

I also remember the host of medications adults were taking, antidepressants, tranquillisers, digestive tablets, PPIs, antibiotics; the list is long. Little did I know that I was suffering from stress too, covered in eczema from birth, bullied in school, and freaking out when faced with exams, I certainly was. Once I reached my teenage years, it slowly dawned on me that the root of stress lay somewhere within people and, therefore, within me.

Had I inherited a stress reaction, like my dad's ginger hair or had I learnt a rather useless way to react which did not serve me well at all? My journey along this path of discovery started in my early twenties, and I have been looking for answers ever since, accumulating thoughts, ideas and learnings along with science and people's stories.

As you might have gleaned by now, I come from a stress-prone family, and most of us never learnt any means or ways how to best deal with stress naturally.

Unlike the rest of my family, I took the natural path, relying on herbs and homoeopathy rather than medication.

I continued perfecting my knowledge, digging deep and unearthing great teachings from around the world.

Unfortunately, my father and brother did not take heed, and I sadly lost them both to stress-related diseases.

When we buried my little brother in 2019, a death which was totally preventable, my book on stress was born.

Dedication

This book is dedicated in gratitude to my "little" brother.

So grateful that I had the privilege of meeting you on this beautiful earth you called home for a little while.

Acknowledgement

A big thank you to all the wonderful people who contributed to this book.

The contributions from the Public who wanted to stay anonymous, thank you for your honesty and sharing your experiences with stress.

Thank you to all the Co-Authors who so generously donated their knowledge and expertise in their wonderful articles, enriching this book with their specialists' input.

Thank you: Elke Wallace, Fenella Hemus (MABNLP, MTLT, MABH), Su Winsbury, Ramona Stronach, Nicole Price, Tina Bakardzhieva, Laurence Nicholson FRSA,(Global- Award Winning "Proactive Burnout Prevention & Recovery Coach, Behavioural ,Leadership & Corporate Wellness Coach, Tracey Secker and Beverly Radley.

A special thank you goes to The Book Chief Publishing House. I really appreciate their constant support and encouragement, without which I would probably still be thinking about writing this book instead of actually doing it.

Thanks for holding my hand throughout!

Introduction

We all get stressed at times; it's what we know and how we deal with it which makes all the difference.

Finding our way through our stresses and stressors can feel like wandering through a maze. It can feel daunting and downright scary when we don't know where to begin and repeatedly find ourselves back at square one in the midst of a stress response, stuck for a solution.

The aim of this book is to shine a light on the plethora of possible stressors and increase your awareness of how stress responses can affect your body - mind - emotion - spirit axis - before it comes to the final breaking point.

You will find scientific explanations, people's stories of their own experiences with stress and the insights they gained. Continuing my way with all things natural, we will hear opinions and learn strategies from specialists in the non-medical field.

This book will provide you with pointers and tools to help you make better choices and provide you with solutions you might not have considered before.

Knowledge is power, power to help yourself. We shall explore the very real and intricate stress response patterns in the presence of major life events and why it is possible that we can still suffer from stress in the absence of those events.

We will explore inner stressors, from our physical body to our brain, to our thoughts and emotions and how they all interact.

We will also take outer stressors into consideration, those we think we have no control over, like the people around us, relationships, work and home environment, and explore how we interact and what we can do to help ourselves.

We will also delve into how the past can affect us and how we can move into a calmer future self.

NB: DISCLAIMER:
The book does not present as a scientific work; it is a collection and reflection of people's views, thoughts and lived experiences

SECTION ONE

Stress and Stress Response, the common culprits

The official idea, often cited by the media and acknowledged by the medical community, is that certain life events impact us negatively and can be very stressful.

For example, events like bereavement, job loss, marriage / relationship breakups, loss of income moving house, and serious illness, not to mention natural disasters and wars, can impact our wellbeing and contribute to ill health, resulting in a plethora of health issues.

Statistics

According to a YouGov study from 2018 about the impacts of stress (taken from across the whole of the UK, sample size 4,619 respondents).

- 74% of people stated they felt so stressed that they felt overwhelmed and unable to cope.
- 30% of older people never feel overwhelmed compared to 7% of young adults.
- 46% ate or drank too much or unhealthily because they were stressed

- 29% reported to have started or increased alcohol and smoking

In addition, of those who reported feeling stressed: 36% stated this led to depression and 61% reported a feeling of anxiety

For 18–24-year-olds the reason for high levels of stress were comparing themselves to others, the pressure to succeed and housing worries.

Interestingly for 12% the feeling of having to respond to messages instantly was cited as a source of stress.

For 36% of adults worries about their own or family member's health was a source of stress which rose to 44% for adults over 55.

According to Ciphr (HR software) studies in 2021 using Censuswide (research company) asking 2000 adults how stressed they felt each month:
- 79% feel stressed at least one day a month
- 7% feel stressed every single day
- and one in five feel stressed more days than they don't.
- 39% cite lack of sleep and money worries as the main stressors
- 23% say that work in general makes them feel stressed

- 18% find that workload and other demands are the main reason for stress

The tiger chasing us

A further commonly accepted idea is that we are hard-wired by default to respond strongly to a real or perceived threat. In the famous story of a tiger chasing us, we have to make a split-second decision about how to react.

In an effort to keep us safe, our system releases Adrenalin and Cortisol into the body, shutting down all unimportant functions, like digestion, and instead releasing energy to important structures and organs such as the heart, muscles, and the brain, to enable us to fight, flee or freeze, and the most recently added response of fawning.

This simple explanation of what constitutes a stress response seems incomplete and does not go deep enough for us to grasp what is really going on behind the scenes.

In my experience, stress affects everything, within and without us. Our thoughts, emotions and moods elicit the same physical reaction as the tiger would.

All is connected, and our body and brain are on a constant feedback loop, in an attempt to keep us safe and in balance.

We are designed to deal with short-term stressors; in fact, they can improve our energy, resilience and stress resistance. They train our mind and body, increasing mental and emotional resilience and improving our immune system reactions.

However, long-term exposure to stress will damage us.

We are hardwired for survival, and the ability to respond quickly and efficiently will give us extra power, strength and speed.

Short-term stress, although not always pleasant, will be dealt with quickly throughout the body. A quick release of adrenalin and cortisol to give us the extra energy, strength and sharpness of mind, and off we go in high-performance mode; whether that's a presentation or a job interview, running to catch the train, or just taking on an extra task in the middle of everything else, it's no problem. You give that presentation, and when it's over, you feel elated, pleased with yourself and happy; your body calms down, and you are back to normal within a short space of time. Once you catch the train, your heartbeat and breathing slow down and you can happily enjoy your journey. No harm done!

"Stress is the trash of modern life, but if you don't dispose of it properly, it will pile up and overtake your life"
(Danzae Pace)

However, long-term stress, no matter where and how it arises, will damage our whole being and impair our ability to thrive. If we are not chased by a tiger nowadays, what produces that reaction?

Our body responds to various triggers, which could be physical but also to our own internal thoughts, worries, fears, unprocessed emotions and much more.

The thing is, you do not have to feel stressed for a physiological stress response to be taking place and for changes to happen in your body, most of which run beneath your awareness. Only when the body throws up symptoms will it come into your field of awareness.

"How do you know you are stressed?"

Find your TELL:

Your "Tell" are the early warning signs and symptoms in your physical, mental, and emotional body to signal that something needs to be addressed. We are all wired differently, and we therefore present with a wide array of symptoms depending on the person.

Getting to know one's tell is the easiest way to break a stress cycle by taking preventative steps to avoid ill health on all levels. You will be able to sidestep overwhelm, breakdowns, burn outs and many more physical, mental, and emotional reactions in your system produced or impacted by stress.

My Stress Tell

Signs and symptoms checklist:

- bloating
- IBS
- acid reflux
- constipation
- diarrhea
- undigested food in stools
- craving for sweets/chocolate/carb foods
- drinking alcohol excessively
- increased/re-uptake of smoking
- worrying thoughts
- repetitive thoughts
- frequent headaches
- need to talk incessantly
- anxious feelings and worry
- sweaty hands
- shaking hands
- palpitations
- interrupted sleep
- sleeplessness
- difficulty breathing
- stiff neck /shoulders
- impaired short-term memory
- reoccurring colds and flu/taking a long time to recover from it
- sore throat
- losing temper easily
- angry outbursts
- can't sit still
- trouble concentrating
- brain fog
- frequent tearfulness without apparent reason
- dislike of bright lights
- unable to screen out sounds
- affected by smells
- dislike of busy environments
- inability to cope
- paranoid thoughts
- lower backache
- teeth grinding at night
- tense jaw
- difficulty swallowing
- difficulty concentrating
- brain fog

this list, it might be a good idea to reflect on
ɘs you have noticed within yourself and
ᴜ increase your awareness

I don't believe we can ever live a life free of stress; however, we can learn how to deal with it and balance out the impact with positive action.

Our body, after all, is constantly trying to maintain homeostasis, call it balance in simple terms, to ensure our survival.

With increased awareness and fitting strategies, we can support our body in doing so.

 Stress occurs when the demands made on an organism exceed that organism's reasonable capacities to fulfil them.
(Hans Selye's...The Stress of Life)

Hans Seyle, a Hungarian scientist, often named the father and inventor of the word stress, spent a lifetime researching and publishing his studies about stress.

He states that, although there seems to be no relationship between our behaviour in connection to our cells, there is strong evidence that all our body systems are impacted, our glands and organ systems, our lymphatic system, and digestive tract, amongst many others.

Thankfully since then, much more research has been done into human stress responses, and we have increased our understanding of our brain functions/malfunctions under stress, and the impact of physical, emotional and mental states.

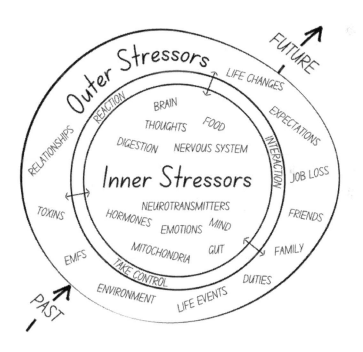

Stress stacking and overload

"I need to get to the bottom of this thing called stress and find out what I can do about it.

When I hear the word stress, what instantly springs to mind is too much to do, too many obligations, having taken on too much work.

Kids screaming, I am pulling my hair out, and my boyfriend storms off in a huff, or sometimes the other way round.

I cannot cope, I cannot sleep, I always get a rash when I am stressed, lose interest in sex, I just need to stay in bed and sleep. It goes on and on, and sometimes I feel totally out of control." *(T from Berks)*

This is a typical reaction when we are experiencing an overload.

Lesion stacking of stress

A process where one by one, we build from a single and acceptable stressor we can deal with, to an accumulation which becomes too much.

We only notice stress from the final reaction, when we reach tipping point, we become aware of it.

In reality, inner layers of stress have been stacking up for a while, sometimes a lifetime.

Knowing and dealing with those layers is important to avoid an overload.

In a state of high alert, we first need to calm down
This will enable us to think straight and get to the bottom of what really stresses us out.

The calming tools:
meditation, visualisation, and mindfulness
Public awareness of those practices has thankfully risen during covid and the ensuing lockdown.

Many apps and online courses have become available, and with regular practice, they will help you to clear your mind and keep calm.

Many studies show they reduce the harmful effects of prolonged stress hormone exposure (which stimulates the release of inflammatory cytokines which in turn will eventually cause systemic inflammation impacting all body systems).

Through meditation, mindfulness and visualisations, we resume control of our nervous system response, control our thoughts, and give our mind and body much needed respite and the chance to return to a calm state of concentration, relaxed muscles and deeper breathing.

I love visualisations and state change exercises.

They will give you control over how you want to feel and enable you to continue your day in a peaceful and re-energised way.

VISUALISATION

A calm anchor in your busy life
Find a comfortable position in a quiet spot. Now cast your mind to your favourite place in nature, a beach, park, woods, anywhere you know you can feel safe and relaxed.

Start creating your own little heaven on earth.

Breathe in and out, let your breath flow naturally and imagine your little heaven, create it in every detail.

Are there trees, plants, flowers, or are you near water, the sea maybe?

What can you smell?

What colours do you notice?

What can you hear?

How do you feel in this special place?

How is your body, is it relaxed, smooth, and comfortable, or is there any tension of knotted muscles or pain and restriction?

Take note and let it go.

Breathe.
Any thoughts and emotions rising?
Notice them, say thank you and let them drift through.
Return to your breath, notice it, take one last look around your safe, relaxing space, then come back to yourself.

How are you feeling now?

Try this several times while reading this book.

With practice, you will be able to do this even in a crowded place, taking a fraction of time to calm you down.

Stress

*sometimes stress can be
Thinking that you'll lose your friends
Moving some where else*

*Having no time for work
Not having enough sleep time
NO control of life*

(N....9years old)

Stress is Personal

We are not all built the same way; our DNA, upbringing and life experiences have shaped us into unique beings. Therefore, how stress impacts us on a physical, psychological, mental and emotional level differs from person to person. One of the most important steps we can take is to identify our own individual stressors and recognise how they impact us.

 "The intensity of our stress experience and its long-term consequences depend on many factors unique to each individual" (Dr. Garbor Mate, When the Body Says No)

REAL LIFE EXPERIENCE

Concentrate on the positive

I never get stressed; at least I didn't think I was. I used to say: "I'm happy when my body is happy". I never used to get ill apart from two colds a year, and until recently, I did not realise that my signs of stress are sleepless nights, awake at all times, thinking and worrying about things, which makes me very tired and ratty the next day and impatient at work. I also get an upset stomach and get bloated and uncomfortable all round. I know now that my body is telling me something.

My new saying is: "My body is happy when my brain is happy", and I have learnt a few new things along the way, like stop and breathe, don't rush my food, let things go, and concentrate on the positive. *(B from Slough)*

SECTION TWO

Feedback Mechanisms

Chapter 1

The Impact of Stress

By Elke Wallace

What is Stress?

Introduction

In our fast-moving world of the 21st century, stress has become more and more common among people, affecting both mental and physiological health. According to a 2018 study by the Mental Health Foundation UK, 74% of people have felt so stressed they have been overwhelmed or unable to cope. We can assume the percentage may have increased even further due to the COVID Pandemic.

In the following paragraphs, I will explore different aspects about stress, where it occurs, what happens in our bodies, how we react to it and how it can affect our lives. As a qualified Neuro Agility Practitioner, I will focus a lot on the brain in the context of stress.

When does stress occur?

Stress can affect us at all different stages of life and is not limited to any sex, gender, or cultural background.

We can feel stressed about minor events and situations, especially new and unfamiliar situations like meeting new people, entering a new environment like a new workplace, giving a public talk or when the unknown strikes with unforeseen news.

Bigger life events like the death of life partners, family members or friends, marriage, separation or divorce, changes at work, starting a new job, new managers, retirement or being made redundant, serious health problems or life-altering injuries, court cases or jail terms, financial problems, parenting issues, relocations and house moves, etc. can expose us to more prolonged stress.

Other things considered stressors which can influence or add to our stress levels and affect us, and especially the functionality of our brain, include: unhealthy diet and nutrition, and in particular food full of additives, flavourings, colourings or sweeteners, our physical environment, Electro-Magnetic Frequencies (EMFs), drugs and medications, developmental hindrances, school and education, and habitual negativity.

Our internal warning system
Our body and brain have evolved over thousands of years. In ancient times, and aided by our heart and gut (often called "our other two brains"), our clever brain, with its inbuilt warning

system, prepared us to fight, run, or hide immediate dangers like wild animals, warrir dangerous plants.

Our senses (vision, hearing, touch, smell, taste) would ue. something that did not look, sound, feel, taste, or smell right, or maybe something nearby made us feel uneasy with a reaction in our gut or heart. The information was transmitted to our brain, which then prepared our physiology to act or stay silent.

This internal warning system is still present in our bodies today. We may no longer be exposed to wild animals, but modern 21st-century life may come with other, often invisible or unfamiliar dangers. However, many things our warning system perceives as dangerous do not directly threaten life. A series of negative thoughts, or even just one, can activate the brain's stress response because our brain cannot distinguish between a real-life event and thoughts.

What exactly happens during stress?
To better understand how the stress response works and why it has such a profound effect on our body and the way we think and act, let's take a closer, in-depth look at the process.

...ive information via our senses or signals from our gut ...eart; the information is then transmitted to our brain via ...eural connections and the nervous system.

In our brain, the Amygdala, part of the ancient so-called "reptilian brain", checks in with the Hippocampus, where memory is stored, whether it is something familiar or unfamiliar. If something unfamiliar is detected, which cannot be resolved with a solution from stored memories in the Hippocampus, the Amygdala perceives it as danger and activates the process of the stress response.

Inhibiting brain chemicals and neurotransmitters like Cortisol and Adrenaline are secreted. Cortisol reduces or shuts down the transmission of messages to certain brain regions not involved with the stress response, and activity in those brain regions will be shut down. Adrenaline meanwhile, will help get the body ready to fight or flight, and those brain regions involved with the stress response remain active.

The heart rate increases and more blood is transported to the limbs in preparation for action, while the immune system, responsible for the renewal, regeneration and maintenance of the body, is drastically reduced, or even shut down, to divert all energy to the stress response.

How do we react to stress?

We are all unique individuals with different DNA, body composition, and differently wired brains. The way our brains developed, are wired, and work is not solely based on our genetic makeup.

How we nurture our brain, by means of adequate sleep, nutrition, stimulation and increased oxygen uptake through movement and brain fitness exercises has a huge impact. As does our general attitude, past experiences, conditioning and what we watch, read, listen to, etc.

Research shows that different reactions to stress can be based on a person's neurological design.

For example, if a person has a left-brain hemisphere dominance, they may react differently than a person with a right brain hemisphere dominance. A more expressive or extrovert person may react differently to a more introverted or receptive person.

The left hemisphere is more focused on logic, language, facts, details, planning, etc. and controls the right side of the body. Therefore, when people with a left-brain dominance experience stress, they focus more on facts, want to understand details or aspects of the event or situation, and think in a very analytical way. They may choose to put their thoughts into writing or express them by talking, and they can come across as tense or insensitive towards other people. In the event of stress, their right brain hemisphere is the area that gets inhibited or shut down by the increased secretion of Cortisol.

The right hemisphere deals with creativity, emotions, practical, holistic, social and people-oriented aspects and controls the left side of the body. Therefore, when right-brain-dominant people experience stress, their focus is more on the big picture of the situation or event. They experience the emotions of the stress situation, but language may not be their preferred initial response, despite feeling a strong need to express those emotions or to physically move. These people may come across as if they act without thinking straight or remembering details, and appear very emotional yet find it difficult to express emotions. In the event of stress, their left-brain hemisphere is the area that gets inhibited or shut down by the increased secretion of Cortisol.

More expressive people may talk more and louder, while more receptive people may talk less, stop talking or withdraw completely.

People in "fight mode" become more aggressive when stressed, people in "flight mode" want to run away or remove themselves from stressful situations, and people in "freeze" mode shut down, withdraw, or get very quiet.

Impact of stress on relationships

Stress can have a profound and negative impact on how we think, act, and behave, especially when we interact with other people around us, whether at work, at home or in other situations.

Possible responses and behaviours that can indicate a person may feel stressed include:

- short, sharp, snappy answers as responses
- easily losing patience with others
- easily getting irritated or angry for insignificant reasons
- getting upset or sad seemingly for seemingly no reason
- being less socially active
- completely withdrawing from people.

Effects of chronic or long-term stress

Short moments of stress can have the positive effect of spurring us on to complete tasks or compete in sports or other activities. However, regularly occurring stressful events or situations, and especially prolonged periods of experienced stress, can seriously affect our overall health and wellbeing.

According to a US study, "75%–90% of human diseases are related to the activation of stress system". Long-term and chronic stress can cause many serious health problems like clogged arteries, restricted blood flow and circulation problems, as well as heart disease.

Stress blocks the electrical transmission of messages in our brain, kills brain cells and affects brain circuits, i.e., our ability and capacity to learn, memorise and remember things. When we experience acute stress, we may temporarily not quickly remember what we usually know well when we are calm and balanced.

The most profound effect long-term stress can have on our body is the reduced functionality of our immune system, which is responsible for cell renewal, keeping the organs in working order and fighting off harmful intruders like bacteria, viruses, and germs. If our immune system faces constant disruption, if we keep living in the survival mode of fight, flight, or freeze, we may become prone to not only the diminishing of our brain capacity but may develop other serious life-threatening physiological diseases and mental illness.

How mindset and attitude can influence stress levels
As previously mentioned, our brain cannot distinguish between a thought and something that is really happening. That's why it

is very important to keep your thoughts, mindset, and attitude in check and to work on developing a positive mindset and attitude.

An overly negative mindset and attitude may make us experience stress more quickly and possibly in a more intense way.

Living with a mainly negative outlook on life, exposed to constant negative media reporting, as well as limiting beliefs and thought processes, produces a similar effect to stress on our brain and biochemistry. According to neuroscience research, a high exposure to negativity increases the production and secretion of Cortisol, which as we heard before, inhibits the transmission of electrochemical messages throughout the brain – with a knock-on effect to our physiology.

A negative mindset and attitude can therefore contribute to the development of chronic stress and lead to more serious implications on long-term health and wellness.

Working on and developing a positive mindset and outlook on life is key, and your overall health will thank you for making the effort.

How can I help you?

I am a qualified Neuro Agility™ Practitioner, Performance and Mindset Coach and NLP and Timeline Therapy™ Coach Practitioner, with further training in Mindfulness, Cognitive Behavioural Therapy (CBT), and Ho'oponopono (the modernised version).

I will work with you to improve your mindset and attitude and implement stress coping skills you can apply and integrate in your daily life.

The basis of all coaching will be creating your unique Neuro Agility Profile™, which will show you how your brain is wired, how you are processing information in both normal and stressful situations, and how you are currently maintaining your brain health. The profile will be explained to you in detail during a debriefing session.

The further coaching process will then focus on improving your brain health and mindset and on exploring and implementing useful stress coping strategies you can apply in your daily life.

Remember, stress is the brain's biggest enemy and can cause serious long-term health issues and illness if not addressed and if no stress coping skills are introduced and put in place. Your overall health will thank you for taking action and learning how to deal with and cope with stress.

Contact: Elke Wallace,

Performance and Mindset Coach, NLP & Timeline

Therapy™ Coach Practitioner, Neuro Agility™ Practitioner

Business: Mastering Your Mind Matters

Email: elkeawallace@gmail.com

LinkedIn: https://www.linkedin.com/in/elke-a-wallace

"The intricate feedback mechanisms of our mind body and emotions, all trigger-happy to produce a stress response in milliseconds."

Chapter 2

Stress and Nutrition

By Tracey Secker

Which comes first – stress or a poor diet? Like many things about stress, they are interlinked. If we are stressed, our eating habits and nutritional needs may change. This can then lead to our stress not being supported and becoming worse.

So why is this? Well, if we start with the mechanics, stress affects the body's use of calories and nutrients in various ways, as it raises the body's metabolic needs for oxygen and energy and increases the use and excretion of many nutrients.

It can also create a chain reaction of behaviours in us that negatively affects eating patterns; undereating, overeating, compulsive, and harmful eating activities.

Often, we feel we need and want comfort foods during these times, so we eat more processed snacks, sweets, and foods high in fat and calories and low in nutrients. We've all been there, the meeting you know will be stressful, the family gathering, the loss of someone, feeling ill, watching someone we love going through a stressful situation. These and many more things will affect our stress levels, which in turn may mean we don't look after ourselves through our nutrition – then our stress gets worse as we may feel ill, fat, depressed, and lacking energy. A circle of stress and poor nutritional choices that we all recognise.

During these difficult times, we will often skip meals, grabbing quick fixes to stop our perceived hunger requirements. We can find ourselves lacking motivation in all areas of our wellbeing, including looking after ourselves by preparing healthy meals. But the facts are that these things do not help our mental wellbeing and stress levels.

According to a study published in the British Journal of Psychiatry, high consumption of processed fats can increase the risk of depression. Researchers found that people with diets high in processed fats had a 58% higher risk of depression than those who ate whole foods.

Historically, when early humans faced food scarcity they used foods high in fat to give them the calories they needed, and sugar in quick releases of glucose. But today, these quick releases are used more often to combat the stressful situations we described above, from work, relationships, financial issues and, more recently, Covid pressures. We also now have an abundance of food options that provide the wrong nutrients, calories, and sugars, so we are definitely not in the position that early humans were!

Another thing stress can do is disrupt sleep patterns. This often leaves us tired during the day, so what do we do? We reach for the sugary fixes of course – the office biscuits, the sugary energy drinks, hot chocolate because 'it's cold outside, I've had a tough day, and I need a pick-me-up'.

And then there are your coffee breaks and caffeine drink fixes. High consumption of caffeine causes blood glucose levels to fluctuate through increasing cortisol levels and dysregulating insulinotropic polypeptide and GLP-1 (technical stuff right, but simply put, not good for you!). An increase in cortisol will also help to increase the accumulation of fat in the tummy area, which is something called central adiposity. This is linked to insulin resistance and the increased risk of type 2 diabetes, cardiovascular disease, and breast cancers. So, not only could your diet not help in the short term with stress, but in the long term, if you develop one of those health issues, you will have more stress in your life. Not a situation any of us want.

So what are some of the things we can do about this?

Diet

Nutrition and a healthy diet can be used to support the body during times of stress, increasing resilience, building strength and re-equipping the body with nutrients that may become depleted during periods of chronic stress.

For example, research has indicated that magnesium and vitamin B6 may support individuals experiencing stress. A further study by Jahangard et al. (2019 - pubmed.ncbi.nlm.nih.gov) showed that people who were administered omega-3 fatty acids demonstrated reduced psychological and physiological burnout, including decreased cortisol levels. Interesting stuff hey!

Any diet that has a balance of fresh fruit and vegetables is always going to be better for us than one packed with processed foods only. But what foods have which vitamins and nutrients?

Below I have concentrated on vitamins B, C and magnesium to begin with, which will particularly help with stress:

- Vitamin B – this lovely vitamin will provide you with energy after a period of stress. It can be found in meat, fish, bananas, dairy products, seeds, greens and nuts. Oh, and don't forget chickpeas – I love a salmon, chickpea and rocket salad for a pick-me-up at lunchtime.

- Vitamin C – This is largely stored in the adrenal glands, which are responsible for the production of stress hormones. Found in citrus fruits, blackcurrants, tomatoes, peppers, leafy greens and broccoli. And don't forget the much-maligned Brussels sprout – not just for Christmas, you know!
- Magnesium – helps to relax muscles and reduce anxiety. Also helps hormone and energy production, so good for stress and menopause. Found in green leafy vegetables, nuts (particularly Brazil nuts, but limit the amounts as they are also high in fat), beans, lentils and whole grains.

Take a bath with Epsom salts to increase magnesium levels through the skin – put some candles in the room, and your stresses will float away.

Let's look at a few more things now

Complex carbohydrates – these are whole and unprocessed carbohydrates such as wholegrain bread, pasta and cereals, as well as oats and brown rice. They help to enhance levels of serotonin, which is often called the mood-boosting hormone as it helps you to feel happy and more relaxed. Low levels of serotonin in the body are linked to anxiety and depression.

Essential fatty acids – these are Omega 3 and 6, which help the body, and in particular the brain, function effectively. They help to moderate the effects of psychological and physical stress as they lower the release of glucocorticoids (hormones released from the adrenal gland) under stressful conditions. Eat oily fish, nuts and seeds to get these – and as fish is apparently a brain food, you will undoubtedly become a whizz in family quizzes.

Calcium-rich foods – research shows that calcium may be able to help reduce muscle tension and anxiety. So if you include calcium-rich foods in your diet, such as low-fat milk, yoghurt, cheese, leafy greens and broccoli, you will see benefits in stress but also help your bone density in the long run – if you are younger than 40, this will mean little to you now, over that age you will thank us for this piece of advice!

Eat Regularly

We talked about how feeling stressed can sometimes lead to us skipping meals. To help maintain our sugar levels and not feel like going to sleep in the afternoon, we need to eat regularly throughout the day. Don't tell yourself you don't have time for food, that a coffee will be enough, that you'll just grab something quick – eat something quickly if you have to, but make it count to your wellbeing.

Carry a Snack

Having something to munch on when you feel hungry will help you. So have something in your car, office (which could be your house now), or when you are out and about, so you can get that pick-me-up in a healthy way and not with a packet of crisps. You could try some fruit, nuts, carrot sticks, cheese, celery sticks, or even plain popcorn. Research some things online; there are so many you can have!

Plan, plan, plan

I know, you don't have time, I hear you say. But what if you take 10 minutes each day to make lunch – either for home or on the go? It will mean no more grabbing something quick from the cupboard or buying a sandwich that doesn't always taste that great. Give it a go and see how much money you save, how much better you feel in the afternoon, and less stressed when you look in the mirror – because we do feel better when we feel healthier and fitter.

Drink differently

We talked earlier about caffeine in coffee and energy drinks. You may think it makes you feel better, but it also has an effect on your body and, ultimately, how you respond to stress. So, if you want to reduce your stress levels and improve your mental performance throughout the day, you may want to gradually wean yourself off large amounts of caffeine. A way to do that is to replace coffee with decaffeinated green tea, which has a soothing taste and the added benefit of loads of antioxidants.

Try it slowly at first, have a green tea every other drink and then build up from there.

Try sparkling juice or water if you are a fizzy pop drinker. The sugar in full fat fizzy drinks is known, but don't think that low-sugar options are better – hydration is key to feeling better and less stressed during the day, and these types of drinks do not help.

Alcohol, along with other substances, are things we turn to in times of stress. Alcohol may have an instant calming effect on the body, but in the long-term it can increase the amount of stress in our lives – it can lead to addictions, health issues, sleep problems, nervousness, and anxiety. Please try other ways if you feel stressed such as taking a walk in the park. It's cheaper and of more benefit.

Stress is affected by nutrition – whether by it not being helped, or our mental wellbeing being stressed out because our nutritional choices are affecting us. I would always say this – balance, balance, balance.

Food, like life, has to be enjoyable – so have good things balanced with a few naughty things. Eat well, but balance your portions with the amount of exercise you do. If you want to socialise, do it with laughter, conversation and maybe just a main meal and not the starter and dessert.

Contact: Tracey Secker:

Green and Wicked Wellbeing I Facebook

e-mail: greenandwicked@hotmail.com

 "Our system, like a highly sophisticated surveillance centre, tries to keep us safe"

Whatever the reason or source of our stress, our body has only one response, it activates the stress response to physical, biological, and electrical signals as much as to our thoughts and emotions.

Chapter 3

Gut-Brain

By Andrea Ursula Hochgatterer

"Look after your gut your brain will thank you."
Without the right inner environment in your gut, the microbiome, positive bacteria, well-digested food and maximum nutrient uptake, our body will suffer low-grade stress levels as it is not receiving the macro and micronutrients it needs for survival.

Not to mention extra stressors of an overgrowth of nasties like candida or parasites, which will need to be addressed to ensure a healthy functioning gut.

Stress will impact your digestion and gut function, leading to lowered gut defence, inflammation, thinning and eventually breaking the gut lining, leading to a leaky gut resulting in reduced nutrient uptake, allergies and inflammation, adding a further stress load to our body. Your body will stay on high alert as it does not like the uncertainty of lacking nutrients. We cannot talk about the gut without mentioning the brain.

The connection between gut and brain is not an imaginary one but very much a developmental fact.

Gut and brain come from the same tissue. As a developing embryo, we are but one long wormlike structure, the gut at one end and the brain at the opposite side, connected by the nervous system (the gut contains as many nerve cells as our spinal cord).

Gut and brain stay connected and continue to communicate for the rest of our life. Sensations of hunger, satiety, pain, or nausea, even feelings of joy or sadness are conveyed to the brain. The gut, also called the second brain, sends messages in the form of neurotransmitters and hormones to the brain, influencing moods, depression, anxiety, and our ability to concentrate and cope with challenges.

The main communication happens via the Vagus nerve, responsible for all our "rest and digest" functions.

Nothing vague about the Vagus (the wanderer)

The Vagus is like a super highway connecting your gut to the brain, innervating on its way areas around the throat and chest, voice box, lungs and heart, digestive system, and the gut; it regulates heart rate, blood pressure, sweating and speaking, your digestion and waste elimination.

It is part of the PNS (parasympathetic nervous system), which is responsible for all calm, "rest and digest" functions; however, the SNS (sympathetic nervous system) will always override the PNS to keep us safe.

Who needs to eat and sleep in the face of danger?

To support our Vagus nerve and activate a quick switch to calm, try:

- Alternate holding your breath and deep breathing
- Gargling and humming
- Essential oils: smell or apply behind your ears.
- A gentle ear pull

Chapter 4

Mitochondria

By Andrea Ursula Hochgatterer

Even Powerhouses Get Stressed

Snippet:

Our mitochondrial DNA comes solely from our mother

Most of us will have come across the term Mitochondria, usually taught in school, and referred to as the powerhouses of the body.

They are tiny, highly efficient, sophisticated structures within all our body cells (apart from red blood cells) and have the sole purpose of turning glucose, the end product of our carb digestion, into energy. They need oxygen, micronutrients, enzymes, vitamins, minerals, and co-factors to function efficiently and produce ATP (adenosine triphosphate) which is the energy our cells can use. They also function as signal molecules in and outside our cells.

In the absence of Oxygen, ADP (adenosine diphosphate) is produced, which is much less efficient (hence keep breathing, exercising and getting fresh air). If not enough energy is produced, you will notice, for example, aching muscles after overexercising.

Under chronic stress, our system requires a substantial amount of energy which might explain why in high-stress situations, we might find a breakdown of the whole mind-body system, accounting for chronic fatigue, mental break down and burn out.

If they feel under attack due to changes in their environment through physical and emotional stressors, mitochondria are capable of signalling to each other to shut down to preserve energy.

They are generally so reactive that they adapt their function precisely to where they are required. They can regenerate, change shape, up their production or die, adapting exactly to biochemical and electrical signals from within our body.

To support your mitochondria, use small amounts of temporary stressors to build resilience and stimulate neogenesis (make new ones). Things like:
- Hot/cold treatments (Saunas and cold washes or showers)
- Intermittent Fasting
- Exercise
- Nutrient-dense foods (full of vitamins and minerals)

In the early eighties, I suffered what we now would call a burnout. I was working in a bank, and we were dealing with a massive amount of overtime due to switching paperwork over to a digital system. This meant weeks of late nights and early morning starts with little time for breaks. I could not sleep due to the ongoing stress of needing to get this done. At the same time, I had a busy household to run with demands from my children and husband.

In those days, I was doing everything myself as I saw it as my duty.

To cut a long story short, in the middle of a workday, I suddenly heard a loud droning booming sound in my ears and seconds later, I could no longer see. I started shouting for help, and thankfully there were lots of people around; they called an ambulance, and the first aiders managed to calm me down, my vision thankfully quickly returned. Once in hospital, after all tests were done, they could not find anything really wrong with me apart from very low blood pressure. The doctors diagnosed exhaustion due to stress and prescribed three weeks in a Dr Kneipp natural healing centre.

Dr Kneipp is famous for his system of using water to cure ailments. He was born in the mid-1800s and devised a "water-cure" system to heal himself, and many others, from then incurable diseases like tuberculosis or cholera, and once, a herd of cattle of foot and mouth disease.

It is a system of daily cold-water applications in the form of wraps, treading in cool water, being splashed with cold water and similar, plus daily massages, lymphatic drainage, herbals and lots of rest in-between. Fresh food, of course, and following a strict daily routine under the supervision of doctors and therapists, plus sun, air, and forest bathing.

The doctor there also told me that I would know I was cured when I became angry. I am not an angry person at all and did not believe him until it happened in week three. I remember looking at the shower curtain and thinking it hadn't been cleaned properly. I felt so outraged by this that I stormed into the office, shouting and screaming that I wanted my money back (very embarrassing really).

The smiling doctor replied, "There you are; you are cured now."

He also told me to do everything, but only half the amount I think myself capable of. I have continued for 40 years to look after myself using cold morning washes, breathing, and walking as a daily wellbeing routine. I also continued all the recommended treatments.

I have learnt that my own health comes first, and stressing out is definitely not worth it in the long run. **(H from Austria)**

Chapter 5

HPA axis

By Andrea Ursula Hochgatterer

The HPA axis and stress response

(Hypothalamus- Pituitary- Adrenal axis)

The HPA Axis is one of the best researched and nowadays best understood mechanisms in our neuro-endocrine system (related to nerves and hormones).

It refers to the tight interplay of three glands which receive stress messages from parts of the body and brain.

Messages get sent to the Hypothalamus which releases CRH (corticotropin-releasing hormone) to the pituitary causing the release of ACTH (adrenocorticotropic hormone), which stimulates cortisol release at the adrenals.

This is a normal response to real or perceived stressors designed to keep us safe by way of preparing us for fight, flight, or freeze, whichever is the best option (remember the chasing tiger?).

Via a negative feedback mechanism, when danger is over and cortisol levels drop, the message reaches the hypothalamus, and the body can return to normal.

Long-term activation through persistent stress will suppress our immune system, affects our memory, and can lead to insulin resistance and, therefore, accumulation of fatty tissue (in other words, you'll put on weight).

Chronic cortisol release will become inflammatory to our system, resulting in adrenal fatigue to the point where we run out of energy. The result is chronic inflammatory conditions, exhaustion, and breakdown.

The reticular system RAS
On top of our spinal cord, inside the brain, sits a collection of nerve fibres called the reticular formation. It is responsible for regulating sensory inputs into our brain/hypothalamus (apart from smell which goes to our emotional brain). Its main function is, like a watchdog, to filter what is important and what we can safely ignore for the moment.

For example, high noise levels, not endangering us, can be kept at bay while we need to concentrate; however, if they seem dangerous, they are let through to the hypothalamus to be processed there.

When we sleep, this system will filter out more of the outside input so playing a part in our sleep-wake cycle. The signals go both ways, upwards to activate relevant parts of the brain and downwards into the spinal cord to adjust posture and trigger locomotor (movement) events during flight or fight response.

It is a pretty nifty system as in the presence of heightened awareness during stress response, it will pass on higher amounts of information, producing increased sensory input, like sensitivity to the slightest sound, increased peripheral vision and a general heightened sense of awareness.

Stress

I am writing this short article for those of you who would like to know different ways of dealing with stress and what has helped me in various stressful circumstances - trauma, cancer diagnoses, unexpected sudden death of my husband...

I am a qualified Reiki master/teacher, reflexologist, massage therapist together with other specialisms in the holistic health field. I also volunteered at the Breast Care Unit at North Bristol NHS giving Indian Head Massage, Reiki, and Reflexology treatments for many years.

In 2019 I retired from my work running a Complementary health clinic offering affordable treatments due to a diagnosis of tongue/lymph nodule cancer.

As you can imagine, I was in total shock with the cancer diagnosis being inoperable, radical radiotherapy was the treatment suggested. I was feeling quite fit, and then suddenly life changing decisions had to be considered.

My recipe for stress relief:-
Ingredients - select a few and mix well
Reiki (ray kee) - is a Japanese form of energy healing.

You can find Mainstream Reiki with Andrea Kennedy and Dive into Reiki with Frans Steine at The International House of Reiki on their YouTube channels. Taggart King, founder of Reiki Evolution is on Facebook and www.reiki-evolution.co.uk

Try a daily Reiki practice by following its Precepts: -

The Secret Method of Inviting Happiness through many Blessings
Just for Today…
Do not anger
Do not worry
Be humble
Be honest with your dealings with people
Be compassionate towards yourself and others
The Founder, Mikao Usui 1865 - 1926

Sound Healing
Raise your vibrations, reduce your anxiety.

For example:
Solfeggio healing frequencies, nine different tones in sound that resonate with the human body:

174Hz - Relieves pain and stress
285Hz - Heals tissues and organs

396Hz - Eliminates fear

417Hz - Wipes out negativity

528Hz - Repairs DNA, brings positive transformation

639Hz - Brings love and compassion in Life

741 Hz - Detoxifies cells and organs

852Hz - Awakens intuition, raises energy at cellular level

963Hz - Connects to the Higher Self. Creates room for oneness and unity.

Known as "The frequency of the Gods"

Listen to the offerings of Temple Sounds on their YouTube playlist section for great videos, and the amazing sounds of high-quality crystal quartz singing bowls infused with semi-precious gemstones, with Jeralyn Glass at Crystal Cadence on YouTube.

Sounds to start your day

Music to start your day in gratitude and uplifting vibration by Barry Goldstein on YouTube.

Breath work, meditation, mindfulness - these practices may reduce blood pressure and are an excellent aid for stress relief.

Breathe - slow down - remain calm - breathe...

Thich Nhat Hanh, Dr Wayne Dyer, Louise Hay, and Dr Joe Dispenza are motivational, best-selling authors of self-help publications. Again, you will find their work on YouTube.

Emotional Freedom Technique (EFT)
The Tapping Solution: A Revolutionary System for Stress-Free Living and the Tapping Solution for Pain Relief by Nick Ortner.

Discover easy to follow tapping routines for relief from pain, stress, and anxiety. There are several informative videos on YouTube.

Dance your body alive with Misty Tripoli at Body Groove. It's easy to do, it works and most of all it's fun.

QiGong with Lee Holden
Transform stress and anxiety into inner peace with gentle stretches and moves. Both Misty and Lee's work are demonstrated on YouTube.

Anti-Stress - Forgiveness - Support & Healing
Listen to Ho'oponono with Sandra Rolus on YouTube. A valuable healing tool.

Added Extras:
- Write a Gratitude list, let go of the "to do and bucket lists".

- Ask for help and be prepared to change.
- Smile, laugh, garden, declutter. Scream, shout, cry.
- Use essential oils, Epsom salt foot baths, complementary therapies.
- Enjoy products made with LOVE, and thrive.

(T from Bristol) Itec Dip, IHM, Reflexologist, Reiki Master/Teacher

 Just as our immune system has the ability to store memory, so has our body down to the smallest cell.

My body manifests stress into 'flare-ups'

I was diagnosed with an autoimmune disease called Axial Spondylo-arthritis in my early 30s. It took medical professionals about seven years to diagnose me.

Fifteen years later I am aware of the relationship between my "bad habits" and the flare ups of the condition. My worst habit is sacrificing rest, movement, and nutritious eating for getting something done - like coursework.

I'm now at university and have recently had two eye flare-ups. I realised I had been holding on to so much stress to do with my partner. He was diagnosed with cancer after I applied to and was offered a place at university. Being away from home whilst he was undergoing treatment was incredibly difficult for both of us. Every day it kept on, the guilt, the pressure to do really well at uni, to make it all worthwhile, missing my partner and our dog; the pain in my heart when we spoke throughout the day, and he told me what he was going through.

I piled it all on and kept on pushing it down until now. I've had inflammation in my eye twice in three months requiring steroid eye drop treatment. My body hurts, my digestion is messed up, and I can't control my moods, despite meditating twice a day where possible.

Allowing the bad habits to creep in; drinking too much alcohol, eating too much sugar, not exercising, forgoing yoga for lying on my bed and watching a movie, and being too tired to make nutritious food, so I order delivery food – all of this is adding more stress.

When stress creeps in, it brings friends like unwanted guests to a party. They take over, things happen, and it feels like I can't do anything to make it right. I remembered a couple of days ago to tell myself, 'I love you, I forgive you'.

I know all will be OK; one by one the uninvited guests will be asked to leave or will be swapped for invited ones. All will be OK. My partner is coming out on the other side, I'm doing really well at uni, and I'm so grateful for so much. *(L from Bristol)*

This is an example of how stress can worsen and derail a system already impacted by a long-term inflammatory pain condition, a system on a stress loop. The amount of stress being heaped on this person increases the inflammatory response, and the hormonal stress cascade is no longer under control.

Chapter 6

Release your Emotions, feel your Stress Melting Away

By Andrea Ursula Hochgatterer

A Body Approach to Dissolving Stress

Your hand opens and closes

and opens and closes

your deepest presence is

in every small contraction and expansion

the two are beautifully balanced and coordinated as bird's wing.

(Rumi)

We are part of everything, and everything is part of us; some even say we carry the whole universe within ourselves, and I agree.

Just as our universe expands and contracts, the sea ebbs and flows, the moon waxes and wanes, so does our body with the same rhythmic flow of expansion and contraction, opening and closing; this is the eternal life force within us, our strength and potency of health.

This rhythmic motion, the breath of life, is the basis for CST (Craniosacral Therapy); it can be felt throughout the body and informs a CST practitioner of what is happening. As the practitioner starts listening to this rhythm and the body realises it is being listened to, the story unfolds, taking the therapist where attention is needed.

Any disruptions through outside events and our thoughts and emotions, are stored in the intelligent body fluids and tissue structures.

Three levels of listening

At the bony level, the expansion and contraction can be felt as a faster and more solid rhythm in alignment with a more solid, dense body structure, speaking of jarring bones, misalignments and stuck-ness which can cause pain and inflammation.

As we lighten our touch, a slower rhythm, the so-called mid tide, emerges, indicating a different energy field, that of soft tissue, muscle, fascia, and organs. This is the level where tissue stagnation and stuck energy from unprocessed events, become palpable, where the body starts telling its story of thoughts and emotions of our daily life which have imprinted themselves.

These stuck disturbances manifest as reduced energy and suppress the body's own healing capacity.

Inviting the tissues to unwind and resolve those past impacts, encourages gentle processing and letting go of that which is no longer needed. This, in turn, increases the energy flow and natural vitality.

At yet a deeper level, we find the long tide flowing softer. On a wider level, where the physical body seems to melt away, we enter a very slow and wide mode of movement, that of a broader perception, part of the surrounding bigger energy field until we are part of the universe, a sense of stillness descends - we have entered a deep healing space.

Now let's listen and hold space for a system under stress:

The actual treatment
Stress stuck in our body tissue, stuck in every layer, the skin, the fascia, the bones, and the organs, causing sensations of restrictions, pain, fatigue, restlessness, and racing thoughts as much as a racing heartbeat.

Stress which has not been processed, impacting all, the brain, the mind, and the complete body.

We often experience this in the plexi - the solar plexus, for example, where we can feel a knot in the stomach area, disrupted digestion, or we might sometimes feel and interpret it as anxiety.

The whole nervous system is buzzing where before there was calm.

The stress layers have been stacking up, unprocessed, not acknowledged, not dealt with, pushed down for ages.

Where before the body was whispering "help", it now is shouting, "Listen to Me".

So here I am, listening.

As, with a gentle touch I tune into the client's system, making contact at the feet, I realise I am in touch with a highly energised state. The tissue and whole-body energy feels like a buzzing electrical current; the nerve endings are vibrating; quite clearly, there is some kind of systemwide overdrive.

In an effort to bring calm to the storm, I talk the client through a breathing exercise and some grounding from the soles of their feet and tailbone, encouraging them to relax, let go and get back in touch with their own body feeling.

As body energy settles down, it aligns to my slow and steady breath and cranial rhythm as an anchor in the chaos; we have made contact, we start to align.

Verbalisation at this point can be particularly useful as it brings what's running in the back of the mind to the forefront, ready to be processed, and while I listen to the body, the client can listen to themselves talking.

The body tissues start to communicate, first by flagging up superficial physical misalignments, sore muscles, misaligned bones, and some digestive turbulence.

At every "listening post" I can feel fascial unwinding and general realigning happening.

Encouraged by calm and gentle touch, the system starts opening up and a deeper rhythm emerges. The body realises it is being listened to; my touch invites it to tell its story.

A simple, very gentle hold below and above the sacrum (lower back level) is a special place in CST as it holds the steady power of grounding and vital energies.

We reach a level of deeper calm, the tissues relax and expand, breathing again with warmth and steady humming, the powerhouse is switched on again. The client has experienced CST before, and when a slight shaking occurs in their feet and legs, we hold that space in silence, together, and let it happen; we know this is the pent-up energy of stress being processed and released.

The client reports a felt sense of warmth in the pelvic area, a sense of peace and relaxation, a calming of worrying thoughts

The body has more to tell
The liver comes into focus, which I point out to my client and take up position above and below the liver area to get a deeper feeling of what is needed there.

I sense an overworked and very much angry liver, and yes, the client confirms they have been feeling angry but cannot pinpoint a particular reason, just stress maybe?

I employ what is called the emotional welcome technique, where we welcome all emotions, in this case, anger; we thank it for showing up as the liver unwinds and relaxes.

The client takes a very deep breath of relief; the liver is whole again.

I mentally ask the body if anything else wants attention.

An upper body cradle hold is asked for, a contact just under both shoulder blades, which is a wonderful space to hold; not only are we in touch with the spine but also the lungs and the heart, both associated with fear, love, loss, and bereavement. This area can become tight, restricted, and energetically shut down at times of stress (if you have noticed, when stressed, our breath becomes shallow, adopting a held stance, and we certainly don't feel love at that point).

This comforting hold enables the whole area to open up.

A widening and softening of the tissue finally releases emotions which I welcome and thank again for showing up, followed by gently rain of tears from the client, tears releasing stress, bringing relief; without having to know more, we accept and release this particular tension.

As there is no pain or discomfort anywhere else in the body, I gently place my hands on the client's shoulders and check through the system to see if anything else needs attention.

However, there is nothing else today, I invite the client to take a deep breath and gently turn their attention back to the room.

Feedback: "I feel relaxed, very calm and energised now"

Contact: Andrea Ursula Hochgatterer

RCST, Dip CNM, DIP CCST

Mindbodyalignment

Wellbeing Coach, CST Practitioner & Naturopathic Nutritional Therapist.

e-mail: hochgatterera@aol.com

www.mindbodyalignment.co.uk

 I've had a lot of worries in my life, most of which never happened.
(Mark Twain)

Worry, Thoughts and Emotions

So how, in the absence of any real threat, can we still wind ourselves up into stress and anxiety when seemingly nothing has happened?

Negative anticipation, disaster movies running in your head twenty-four seven, and the fear maker of "what if" originates from old learned stories and reactions; if we want to be free of the stress of those old reactions, we need to learn how to deal with them.

Feels like a non-stop battle

I struggle with stress a lot, and I really don't do myself any favours as all I do is bottle it up, which in turn makes me snappy at times. Then I lose sleep over it laying there, my mind going round and round going wild; so I am constantly tired, which stresses me out further. I turn to alcohol to help soothe my demons. It feels like a non-stop battle uphill. It's depressing!

(J from Pittsburg US)

Chapter 7

Getting Real with your Emotions

By Tina Bakardzhieva

Heart racing, tense muscles, inability to focus, uncontrollable thoughts, headache, feelings of worthlessness and lack of control...You're feeling STRESSED!

Stress is the sensation of being under an excessive amount of mental or emotional pressure. Pressure then turns into stress once you're feeling unable to cope. When you say, "I'm stressed", you'll also mean you're feeling:

- afraid
- confused
- vulnerable
- sceptical
- worried - the list goes on and on.

Ask yourself this: how often do you go through your day completely unaware of what you're feeling? Like most people, you're probably so busy that you simply don't pause to check in with yourself. After you label your emotions accurately, you've got a tool that helps to manoeuvre forward proactively with the truth you face. You can accept whatever is present without trying to change it, you accept the raw emotion.

It is dangerous to just muddle through the mist of overwhelming emotions, ignore them, and begin puzzling over how everything will be okay on the opposite side. In fact, that's very unhealthy!

Reality will always have its way

People who are bottling up their emotions are usually very focused on doing "what they're supposed to do". They haven't got to grips with their real self and emotions in years, which blocks them from making any potential change or achieving personal growth. Bottling up feels as if it gives us control, but actually, it denies us control. It's like closing a door behind a burning room: suddenly, there's no fire in sight, and we feel safe, but eventually, it'll come out to burn down the entire house around us.

Other people are cognisant of their emotions, and they're literally feeling all of their feelings. They get totally absorbed by their emotions; they simply can't walk out on them. These people can even reach a state where they worry most about the fact that they worry!

They are more likely to succumb to self-blame, feeding their mind with questions like, "Why do I prefer this?" or "Why does this keep happening to me?" Don't get me wrong, asking such questions is super-important, but analysing with no outcomes or decisions is pointless.

How can we get real with our emotions?
It is all about finding an open and honest way to endure them with awareness and acceptance.

First comes the understanding that our feelings aren't who we are. Your thoughts aren't your reality. Reaching this understanding isn't easy - it may seem a cliché, but it is hard to mitigate and register what's actually occurring. Creating a space between our sentiments and also controlling the way we answer them.

Instead of saying "I am anxious", say "I'm feeling anxious". You're rather more than your emotions.

It's freeing! Get comfortable with feeling uncomfortable. Yes, it's difficult in the first place, but the more you do it, the more you permit yourself to accommodate this activity, and the more of a habit it becomes. Then there's nothing scary left because you'll be able to face any emotion.

Every emotion comes in a range of intensities. When someone describes their emotion as anger, they may be just annoyed or impatient. This insight may transform your perception of how others are experiencing emotion, and you'll learn to react to a selected emotion without getting emotional yourself.

In my hypnotherapy practice, I help people create awareness and gain control through simple exercises. For instance, whenever you begin to feel a difficult emotion creeping in, you'll be able to do a two-step practice so as to effectively understand and handle it.

First, try and understand a minimum of two other emotions you identify with. If your initial thought is "I'm stressed," what are two other options that match how you are feeling at that moment? Remember to be specific; in this way, you will be able to get to the heart of what you are feeling instead of putting on a large "stress" label with no actionable ways to handle it. Once you identify those underlying emotions, you're not stuck in, "I am stressed," instead you perhaps recognise, "I am exhausted, so I want greater levels of self-care". It's totally different from just being stressed.

The next step is to find what value the emotion has for you. We tend not to have strong emotions about things we do not care about, and difficult feelings can shed light on what's important to you.

As an example, if you're lonely, do you crave social connection? Are you missing meaningful conversations with your partner or your friends?

Getting real with our emotions means facing up to our worst demons and putting them in their place.

Look them in the eye and say: "hey, you're here, I'm here, and I won't allow you to make me think I'm worthless." This is often a great way to swiftly manage unhelpful emotions.

We battle many demons throughout our life. Many of them are small, and some of them may be large enough to besiege us for months or even years. Finding the proper way to label them may be difficult but, eventually, we'll know exactly what name is fitting. They may often be the demon named "I don't have any self-esteem", "I have an unfulfilling job", "I miss my friends", or "I feel I have no purpose in life".

Probably the most difficult demon's name is "I'm not happy". Try the 2-step exercise I recommended above and find a better label for it.

There's another great hypnotherapy-inspired exercise for practicing awareness of your experience, at least once a day, every day, take some 10 minutes to practice this routine.

Start out by closing your eyes.

To get centred – start by observing what it feels like to be sitting, e.g. what your skin feels as it rests on the chair. Then shift to observing the physical sensations of breathing. Follow your breath and visualise your breathing, e.g. picture what the air coming into your nose may look like.

Spend the next 5 minutes noticing your physical sensations and thoughts.

"Watch" whatever thoughts, feelings, evaluations, memories, sensations, etc, come up without trying to change them at all. After you start looking "from" your thoughts or looking "in" your thoughts, gently bring your attention back to watching your thoughts. Let your thoughts come and go as they please. Accept all parts of your experience.

Finally, bring yourself back to the present by opening your eyes and describing your physical surroundings. If you have a window, look out of the window and describe what you see.

Learning ways to label emotions with a more nuanced vocabulary will be transformative. People who can identify the complete spectrum of emotion, who realise how sadness differs from boredom, pity, loneliness, or nervousness, do far better at managing the ups and downs of ordinary existence than those who see everything in black and white.

Next time you are feeling stressed, attempt to dig a touch deeper into what's hiding underneath rather than relying on general, unhelpful labels.

Contact: Tina Bakardzhieva
Clinical Hypnotherapist
Web: www.oxfordspireshypnotherapy

SECTION THREE

External Stressors

Not all of our stressors come from the inside; there are outside influences, situations, and events we have no control over.

From bereavement to menopause, job loss or serious life-threatening illness, they are confusing and frightening; our life as we know it is changing; change can be stressful, and we feel out of control.

However, we do have control over our reactions and, therefore, actions.

By learning strategies of how to respond to keep ourselves grounded in the positive, we can keep ourselves sailing on an even keel.

Where our minds, emotions, and environments collide

I have managed to learn how to cope with most of life's stressors; however, a book by Jason Hickel, an account of what is really going on in the world, really started to stress me out.

It made me think of a world where my kids have no future, no children of their own even if they wished to, a world where they might witness some horrific situation. It was so painful that I needed to learn many different new techniques to cope with the stress of this new realisation.

People say that sometimes it only takes one book to change everything, and, in my case, it was 'Less is More. How Degrowth will Save the World'. By Jason Hickel.

I have always felt the 'fin de siècle '(end of century) fear that was expressed by some philosophers at the end 19th century - a reaction to the Industrial Revolution and the development of technology. I have always feared that this civilisation needs to end, just like others have throughout the centuries.

I have always felt that there is something wrong with the whole 'growth 'economy. 'How can we continue to grow ALL THE

TIME? It's not natural'. It really scared me, especially when I was a young girl. GDP, GDP, GDP - up, up, up. And when it's down, it means crisis, poverty, etc. that's what I learnt at school, that's what I heard in the news.

But in my heart, I feared the big boom because there are always limits to every growth - people, animals, and plants, grow and stop to enjoy their maturity.

After communism ended, it became even worse. Suddenly, in my hometown of five thousand where the population was static, suddenly there were not just three shops which had been perfectly able to feed the whole population before, but 20!

Suddenly most of the children stopped walking to school together in groups and were driven every day. But our GDP grew, and I was told that we need to buy more, even if it means that some of it needs to be thrown away because then it will grow more, our economy will thrive, we will succeed, and all will be great.

I don't know how or why, but I believed it and seeing more and more cars, and more concrete everywhere, I felt proud because my country was growing. Only a hollow in my stomach, constant anxiety, catastrophic dreams, and expecting something bad to happen, reminded me that maybe it wasn't that great, but I carried on.

However, being around young people and children, I became more aware and started questioning more. For example, why are young people so unhappy these days (or feel unhappy) despite having nearly everything, or access to nearly everything, in comparison to me and my peers?

The pandemic showed that once we stopped travelling and went into lockdown, nature started to thrive. Going for daily walks became a wonderful new routine for many. But the minute it was decided we had to bounce back and 'go back to business as normal'', all of that became nearly impossible because of workloads, traffic, travelling, etc.

And then my sister recommended the Jason Hinkel book to me. I thought I had known everything, disproportion, inequality, rich vs poor. It turns out I knew nothing. I thought that with the zero-emission by 2050 plan, eco equipment, eco cars, and veganism, we were right on track.

I was shocked to discover that we are not only NOT reducing the CO_2 emission, but we are also cutting down more rainforests, producing more meat, and drilling more oil THAN EVER!

And it's not because of the overpopulation in the south, as we are sometimes led to believe. The global north is killing the Earth with the 'Responsibility for Climate Breakdown' (emissions in excess of national fair shares of the 330ppm boundary) as follows the US 40%, Canada 3%, EU and UK 29%, Russia and the rest of Europe 13%, Japan 5% - which adds up 92% for the Global north, but it's the South which is feeling the effects of the global warming right now!

As for GDP – only 1% of the richest individuals enjoy its benefits of it. Leaving us with our gadgets and coffee and chocolate but with the biggest mental health problems ever and a planet whose most wonderful species are becoming extinct EVERY SINGLE DAY, and which will probably become uninhabitable by the end of the century if we don't change drastically NOW.

Change doesn't mean let's go electric and carry on as usual. It means reduce the working week, use public transport, live within earth boundaries.

But seeing what reaction this knowledge brings (no reaction or 'oh so we need to be cave people now'), that there are no sensible laws being passed or even discussed, that climate crisis news are non-existent in media, that people like Greta Thunberg are being laughed at and environmentalists are jailed, and made fun of – I have to think of a world where my kids have no future.

So, we decided to try to make their world as simple and similar to what we had as possible, living in one-day compartments, being thankful for every day where you can see, smell, run, walk, cycle, read, imagine, because it's insane how amazing being alive is. At the same time, live as close to nature as possible, respect it, grow things, and learn it. I now talk about climate change everywhere I can.

This is my solution to deal with the new stress in my life.
(B from Burnham)

Chapter 8

Release Yourself from Stress and Anxiety with NLP

By Fenella Hemus

Frances and Chris were both studying hard for their accountancy exam, and as the date approached, both started to feel increasingly nervous and anxious about it. On the day, Chris felt sick with nerves and nearly didn't go to her exam. Frances

felt nervous too, but channelled her feelings into focusing on doing her best. After all, she'd studied fully, so she knew her stuff. Chris continued to focus on her anxious feelings, which spiralled into thoughts of failing, and her mind went blank during the exam.

Two people with two different experiences of the same event. In both, the stress response was activated, setting off a psychological and physiological chain reaction. This response is part of our autonomic nervous system, so it's not something we can stop. It activates out of our awareness, moments before our conscious mind catches up to what's going on.

The thing that matters is what follows, this being how we react or respond to the stress response. It's something we learn through our early life experiences and from significant adults. It's affected by our beliefs, memories, thinking patterns and self-awareness and through our current influences and environment. Think about it, the word 'stress' is now so commonly used, that even just saying or hearing the word can set off that psychological chain reaction!

Our brain, and within it our mind, is a 'pattern-making machine'. It builds patterns (strategies and habits) to save time and energy in decision making and taking action. This is a good thing.

Can you imagine what life would be like if we had to think consciously about everything we wanted our body to do?

We'd not get much done! Yet this pattern-making, or shortcuts in thinking, also means our mind is prone to faulty thinking and applying outdated, unhelpful patterns to current situations. More about that later.

However, knowing that our reaction to the stress response is a pattern we create in our mind is good news because it means we can change the pattern with our mind. This is where NLP (Neuro Linguistic Programming) comes in.

What is NLP?

For those who aren't familiar, NLP is essentially a user manual for the mind. It's the practice of understanding the thought processes, behaviour and language we use and how they influence the results we get. NLP includes many 'tools 'that can be used to make permanent desired changes to our thinking and behaviour, including how we perceive and respond to pressure and stressors. In order to explain how NLP is really effective for doing this, it helps to understand how our mind works.

The truth is that none of us experiences reality directly; we make up our own version of reality in our head! We take in information via our five senses and only select certain parts, usually the ones that fit with our existing view, which was itself previously created through past experiences. So information gets filtered in or out depending on our values, beliefs, memories, personal preferences, attitudes, language and perceptions about things like time and space. Each of us has our own model of the world that we've created inside our mind.

In effect then, the way we perceive the world is a reflection of how we think and feel inside. Our mind operates from predictions and best guesses, unless we consciously question what we think, feel and do.

Consequently, if we repeatedly react to stressors unconsciously with feelings of anxiety, frustration or irritation, the neural pathway for that response pattern becomes stronger and it gets deeply wired in.

We can even stress ourselves out with our own beliefs and expectations of how we 'should' behave or what we 'should' be, do and have, often comparing ourselves unfairly in relation to others. Such behaviour patterns are learned when we're young, through our experiences and relationships. Moreover, we can learn anxious or depressive behaviours through experiencing our parents' own behaviours or treatment towards us. One of the primary reasons clients come to see me is because they feel highly stressed, anxious or fearful a lot of the time.

Yet experiencing stress is good for us. Yes, I said that! It's good for us. For children and young people, exposure to everyday stressors teaches their brains how to deal with more intense stressors later on. It builds adaptability and resilience, so strengthening the immune system, things that are vital for living well in a fast-changing and increasingly complex world. Uncertainty and pressures are an unavoidable part of life. The stress response is simply a signal telling us that we need to pay attention and take action to change or adapt our behaviour in order to accommodate or deal with a stressor. It's certainly not something to be avoided or totally prevented.

Therefore, the effects of the stress response come largely from our reaction or response to the stress response.

Responding with a flexibility in thinking and behaviour increases choice. These are things that are developed with NLP. One of the accepted beliefs or assumptions is that we all have all the resources inside we need to succeed, and all unwanted limiting responses, habits and behaviours can be changed if that's what we want. From an NLP perspective, the healthy approach to the stress response is to recognise and accept it, then refocus towards your desired outcome and take action accordingly.

Changing perception

As you have heard already, our thoughts set off a chemical reaction, which creates a certain physiology, which results in a behaviour. If we want to change it, we need to interrupt the pattern. The stress response releases energy because it's preparing us for action. We can channel that energy and focus in a positive way, just as Chris did in the story above, as an athlete does in competition or an actor or presenter does before they go on stage.

We can reframe the stress response by taking a different perspective and choosing to have a different expectation. For example, we may always get triggered by a certain tone of voice or words used by family members or someone at work. That trigger was likely created back in childhood when we were criticised or belittled, and our mind took note and anchored it into our psyche. In any similar situation, the mind will trawl through its memory files and pick out the internal representation of that experience, which elicits the same response. Our brain is predicting what's about to happen next and is trying to protect us, even though now, as an adult, the pattern is hindering us. Therefore, if we change the context or meaning and our expectation, we change the response.

Changing the internal representation

When you're in a situation where you feel pressured or anxious, such as a big presentation, an intimidating boss, a confrontation or dealing with anything you fear, you'll have an internal representation made up of images, words, sounds and feelings. Each aspect will have certain details or qualities. For example, the image will be a certain distance, size, brightness, focus and colour, to name a few. This is your sensory representation. When these details are changed, they make a difference. Imagine now a scary boss, angry-faced, looming over you, shouting. The image is likely to be close, big and with certain sounds. If, in your mind, you pushed or threw it far away, making it small and dark, with the voice becoming a tiny squeak or disappearing totally, then your feelings of fear and anxiety will decrease or disappear.

Focusing on what you want

Anything new or unknown activates the stress response in all of us, though we may not notice it. For some, this leads them to imagine all the things that could go wrong and not what could go right or well. Essentially, they are rehearing what they don't want to happen, which creates the same chemical reaction they would have if these things actually did occur. Cue anxiety.

In NLP, we encourage people to focus on the outcome they DO want and to visually rehearse that, which gets rid of the anxious feelings. Here's how. First, think of the event you're feeling anxious about and close your eyes. Imagine yourself going out into the future to 15 minutes after the SUCCESSFUL completion of the event or challenge you WERE feeling anxious or stressed about. See what you'll see, hear what you'll hear or be saying, and notice the feelings generated by the successful completion. Make these feelings as positive and intense as possible. Really be there.

In your mind, turn to face towards now and see all the events between then and now rearranging themselves in support of your SUCCESSFUL outcome. Nice, isn't it? How much more enjoyable it is imagining what you do want, instead of what you don't.

If you don't experience more positive feelings, then you aren't imagining the SUCCESSFUL completion. Are you focusing on what you want? Really? Congratulate yourself on getting through it, and a job well done!

There are many things in the world which are outside our control, and we can waste much time and energy either feeling anxious and worried or trying to control them.

We can't control the beliefs, attitudes and behaviour of other people, just as we often can't control events that take place.

However, we can take charge of how we choose to perceive things and how we think and behave. It's so much more beneficial to focus our energy on the things we can control. Long term, reducing or removing unhelpful responses to stressors increases our resilience and wellbeing.

NLP is hugely effective for changing habitual thinking and behaviour patterns quickly and easily. Therefore it's perfect for reducing anxiety and stress as well as increasing our energy and health. This is why I absolutely love coaching with NLP and teaching others to become NLP practitioners so they can use the 'tools 'and thinking for themselves.

Contact: Fenella Hemus

Certified Trainer of Master NLP, Time Line Therapy™ and Hypnosis and Breakthrough Coaching.

Tel: +44 792 3367545

Email: fenella@fenellahemus.com

Web: www.fenellahemus.com

The stress of life changes, transitions and moving forward

Menopause and stress

Menopause is stressful for many of us – some have lots of symptoms, some a few. Either way, they will cause anxiety, depression and stress.

Due to cortisol and oestrogen imbalances during menopause, our ability to cope with stress is also compromised. Anything that life throws at us could feel worse or heightened - parents getting older with health issues, children leaving home, work pressures, the feeling of invisibility. How rubbish is all of that?

Here are a few things I found increased my stress during menopause and why.

Skin

I noticed when I was about 44 years old, my skin changed. It started as a difference in texture - bumpy to the feel, dry, almost as if I was shaving, which, to be honest, with the hair on my jawline I could have!

Changes were happening daily every morning when I looked in the mirror. Over time it progressed into acne with sore, itchy, angry spots all around my mouth. New ones would come throughout the day, so I was using lots of makeup to hide them, which in turn was making my skin worse.

A merry-go-round where I was left feeling depressed, unattractive and very self-conscious.

Weight gain

When my peri-menopausal symptoms started I was 9 stone, fit, healthy and working at an all-ladies gym. I led regular fitness classes, followed a low-carb diet and often rode my bike to work. So imagine my shock when I began to put on weight with no changes to any of those things.

When I left the gym and went to work in an office, things became worse. Along with the hormone imbalance making my weight increase, I stopped doing as much exercise and was sitting more at a desk and in the car. I also began to comfort eat the office treats – cakes, sweets, crisps. And as my weight continued to rise, my self-esteem declined, and my eating filled a gap.

Merry-go-round number two, please!

Hair loss

One of the joys of menopause is that not only can you grow hair in places it shouldn't be, but it often falls out of places it should be. This is very distressing, but there is also a societal stigma toward women with patchy hair. I know this as I found it at work and with relatives, and my hairdresser has confirmed that other women feel the same.

Hot stuff baby - but not in the right way!

Night sweats and hot flushes are experienced by many women. If it happens during the night, it will disrupt your sleep pattern, which in turn with affect your wellbeing. If it happens through the day, it can be embarrassing due to sweat dripping off your face. You become unable to think about anything else; it can ruin your clothes (blouses with sweat patches aren't a good look) and then people will make you feel invisible by ignoring your requests to open a window or turn down the heating.

Mood swings - I have no idea why I am crying again

I don't remember my teenage years being affected by my hormones as much as when I began perimenopause. One Sunday, I spent the whole day crying. I tried pulling myself together, but nothing worked - I was going to cry and think unreasonable things. I didn't understand it or recognise myself.

Itching in places you don't want to talk about in public

My skin not only decided to cultivate the most awful acne but invited eczema to exist all over my body. I was itchy, scratchy, and grumpy all rolled into one.

More recently, these symptoms have got better, but my dry skin has led to issues in other, more sensitive private areas. An area that we don't like to talk about or admit to.

But I am going to say it for those of you for whom this is also causing stress. I suffer from excruciating vaginal itchiness and soreness. It is so bad sometimes that I can't sit comfortably, it wakes me up in the night, and I have learnt the art of subtle moving around in public to relieve the discomfort!

Feeling weak and forgetting

Body and brain letting you down – muscles feel weak, joints hurt, words and names escape you, and mid-sentence you can't remember what you were thinking.

A few of the things I have tried over the years to ease the symptoms and stop me from riding the 'Menopause Stress Merry-go-round' include:

- Collagen supplements – good for hair, skin and nails.

- Exercise – stretching, yoga, Pilates and building muscles slowly with weights for bones, fitness, muscles and general health.
- Nature – I find walking in nature clears the head and shows you the wonders in the world.
- Getting creative – reading, writing, up-cycling, crafting, anything you want to relax you and give you space.
- Support network – whether this is family, friends, online groups, social groups, just make sure you tell them what you are going through.
- Meditation – this doesn't have to be going to some zen place every hour; it could be 10 minutes of breathing exercises during the day to relieve stress. It could be meditation, mindfulness or relaxation exercises.
- Diet – a balanced diet, Mediterranean is good, lower carb (we all need some carbs), some intermittent fasting. These are all beneficial. *(T from Wolverhampton)*

 There is a path from me to you that I am constantly looking for, so I try to keep it clear as still water does with the moon. (Rumi)

Chapter 9

Taking the Sting Out of Relationships

By Nicole Price

The romantic love relationship

Relationship stress is complex and affects you daily through interactions, particularly with the most important people in your life. It is almost impossible to avoid, unless you are an island, and even then, you create your own stress, putting pressure on yourself.

The disharmony between you and your partner brought on by disagreements and arguments, or what may feel like multiple mini battles with your children, or the frustration you occasionally feel for your parents and siblings. Family get togethers can be the epitome of relationship stress!

Friendship is not always harmonious and carries an amount of stress, even with friends you have known a lifetime. A little bit of stress can be good for you, firing you up, providing focus, even giving you a competitive edge in work or sport-related activities, but too much pressure from a boss or coach, and yourself, can become an anxiety inducing burden.

Life events of great significance, whether happy or sad, put a lot of strain and tension on relationships, bringing their own unique brand of stress. Marriage, moving house, babies, job loss, new job, serious illness, death, separation, and divorce are the most common, and all take their toll.

Stress begins in the brain, evident through your thoughts, actions, and feelings, whilst prolonged stress is felt and manifests itself in your body, displaying as physical symptoms.

You may notice headaches, minor aches, and pains, to more severe symptoms of exhaustion, chronic pain, hormonal imbalances, high blood pressure, anxiety, depression, stroke, and heart attack.

Once you identify how relationship stress is affecting you, the question is, how to manage it?

Stress is often brought on by expectations of people, situations, and desired outcomes. How you feel and respond in those moments is crucial to your wellbeing.

As everyone has free will, the only person you have control over is… you. Your thoughts, feelings, behaviour, are all yours to choose. You may have the ability to influence others, but not control them.

Choose your battles wisely, consider what is important in your relationships, what is worth fighting for, and do not allow the minor annoyances to fester and build up until you erupt, like a volcano.

By reframing your thoughts and behaviours, your relationship with yourself and others will improve whilst also reducing your levels of stress. Be patient and kind with yourself, this will take time as you evolve.

Repressed and negative emotions also live within the body, producing toxins we carry around in the form of anger, guilt, shame, resentment, and bitterness, causing inner stress. Learning to forgive yourself is the way to release these negative emotions and energy from your body.

Richard Carlson's book "Don't Sweat the Small Stuff and It's All Small Stuff" is also a fun, informative read, complete with meditations.

Conscious of them or not, you have expectations placed upon you, many forged during your formative years due to upbringing, and societal norms, a specific way of doing things in a certain order, and acceptable ways of behaving, and in turn, you place expectations on others.

Much stress is caused by anxieties surrounding expectations of people and situations, particularly your passions, relationships, in fact, anything you feel heavily invested in.

When you are attached to desired outcomes, you will try to control and direct in order to bring about your desired resolution. In doing so, you are manipulating a result and possibly ignoring others' wishes.

Continually behaving this way in your romantic relationships can result in resentment and indifference from your partner.

Everyone has masculine and feminine energy within them, a yin and yang that fluctuates in various situations. Masculine energy is action oriented, and feminine energy is receptive.

The feminine tends to be in their masculine energy when at work, managing, taking charge, problem solving, ensuring tasks are completed and resolved, but may find it difficult to switch off at the end of the day, to revert to their natural, receptive feminine energy, when with the masculine. The feminine will often continue in their masculine energy, organising everything at home, from the children to chores and social engagements.

Herein lie the stress inducers...the small, everyday frustrations that build up and boil over.

The feminine and masculine think and approach tasks and life differently. The masculine is wired to view each task as an event, transitioning through each action separately and in order.

The feminine is wired in a way that the same task is seen as one movement, like drawing a circle; the task is complete when the circle is drawn. This may seem simplistic, but once this is acknowledged and accepted, thoughts and requests can be reframed to take account of the differences, developing a more balanced way of understanding and interacting.

The underlying emotions for both masculine and feminine are fear and rejection. Feeling unimportant, unloved, the eventual breakdown of the relationship, and being discarded.

Do you and your partner find yourselves in negative cycles, arguing round and round, blaming each other, without anything being resolved? Asking yourself, "If things will ever change?"

Take the sting out of your relationship with subtle changes that create impact!
A relatively stress-free relationship **is** possible. Not that it is without conflict and challenges, but where both partners feel able to express and be themselves, to discuss issues openly and calmly, without accusations, criticisms or judgement.

There is an amount of stress in every relationship. Learning to recognise the destroyers, the toxic patterns and cycles learned consciously and/or unconsciously is a good place to start. These are continuously repeated and played out in many relationships, for no other reason than that is what we know and have heard in other people's relationships.

I encourage you to ask yourself (and answer truthfully):
"Is it working for you, your partner and your relationship?"
If your answer is "No", I can help you find new ways, a more caring approach that removes the sting from your relationship.

It is not always that your partner stresses you out, but often, the way in which you react and respond to them.

Do not seize opportunities to berate and ridicule your partner but use them as openings to honest and compassionate conversations. This is not to quell the annoyance felt, but by reframing your thoughts and words, the anger and hostility felt by both of you can be reduced or even avoided.

I suggest each partner focuses on their feelings about the situation, "I feel......" which your partner will generally hear, rather than attacking, "You always......" which has your partner on the defensive and unable to focus on the complaint, and you are once again, lost in the eternal argument loop.

Actively listening to one another (not just listening to reply) with empathy and taking responsibility for your mistakes are the first steps towards understanding. Also, be willing to unlearn unhealthy patterns of automatic behaviour.

This is not a quick fix, learning something new always takes time, but being consistent with the changes will create a healthier way of being and release much unwanted stress.

By raising awareness through my sessions, individuals and couples are changing their relationships, their story, from one of despair to a new and improved one, of hope.

Contact: Nicole Price
Relationship Counsellor
Calm Waters Relationship Counselling
Email: calmwaters2022@outlook.com

Interview

I embrace the person who has come out the other side:

Q: Hello A, lovely to meet you again and thank you for agreeing to this interview about stress. You have told me you had your fair share of stress in your life and have found a way of dealing with it in your own fashion.

A: Hi Andrea! Lovely to speak with you too.

I can certainly think of a few situations that I have found immensely stressful, and yes, I have had to make some changes to help me deal with and cope better with stress on a day-to-day basis. I've not fully mastered it yet, but I know I've learnt a few important lessons in managing my stress levels.

Q: Was there a particular time/situation in your life you wanted to share?

A: Yes, I think the most stressful situation was when I was going through a relationship break-up after 18 years of marriage.

I felt trapped, miserable and unhappy in a very controlling relationship. I couldn't see a way out but needed to break away and find a purpose for myself.

I feared breaking up would cause much hurt for my two teenage boys, and I wanted to avoid that. I couldn't bear to turn their life upside down for what seemed like my own selfish reasons.

Around that time, my dad passed away after suffering from a long-term illness (I shared caring for him with my sister) and I was working full time in a stressful job.

Q: I am sorry to hear that A! Such a lot to be dealing with. Did you recognise that you were stressed?
A: I don't think I realised I was suffering from stress at first, but it became apparent that stress was a symptom of my lack of coping and my attitude to it all.

I suffered overwhelmed and saw it as a weakness, not knowing how to deal with it, I expected myself to know all the answers, thinking maybe it's my fault that I don't. Grieving for my dad at the same time, it all rolled into one big feeling of sadness.

Q: Grief and Relationship break-ups are extremely difficult to deal with. Can you remember how your stress manifested itself?
A: I had regular meltdowns and couldn't stop crying; the smallest things would plunge me into a deep dark hole. Some days I just couldn't face getting out of bed, dreading the challenges of the day. I didn't feel emotionally strong enough.

I often wondered if I was suffering from depression but would not take the medication the doctor offered. I didn't want to admit that I needed help, stuck in self-blame and extreme guilt.

So mostly I felt hopeless. I didn't seem to have any control over any part of my life and had no idea if or when things might get better.

I became impatient with people at work, leading to arguments with colleagues.

I suffered palpitations at random times, and even when I felt calm.

I had trouble sleeping, awake in the night stressing about the following day. I noticed a heavy feeling in my chest, which was there most of the time; I can only really describe this as a heavy heartache.

I drank alcohol more excessively in the evenings as it calmed me from all the worry during the day. At the time, I thought it would help me cope.

Q: Did this impact your family, work and relationships?
A: My relationship with my boys in fact strengthened, and to my surprise, they were very grown- up about it all. They reassured

me that it wasn't my fault, and it was OK to start a new life for myself, that I had every right to a happier future.

Relationships at work deteriorated as I could not give my all to my work. I became the subject of gossip spreading which made me angry. I lost my temper at work a few times.

Q: How did the final change come about?
A: When my husband finally accepted my decision and moved out, I was happier, and it brought instant relief.

I felt liberated and free for the first time in my life. I knew it wouldn't be easy, but I took charge with some inner strength.

With him gone, I knew the rest was up to me to fix and rebuild my life

Q: What did you find particularly helpful?
A: I stopped relying on alcohol to feel better, I focused on the positives of each day.

My friends and boys were the best support. I started accepting help and took friends' kind offers of support.

I also had a bit of life coaching, which I found very useful; it helped me deal with my feelings of overwhelming guilt.

Q: How do you deal with stress now?

A: I have decided that life is too short, and I am a lot pickier about what I do, where I work and who I spend time with.
I prioritise and choose how much of me I can give.

I focus on what I can change and how to turn a situation into something positive.

I have learnt to remain calmer and don't resort to arguing or snapping at people. I concentrate on what I can do in a kind way and focus on that rather than losing my head over it.

If I feel palpitations creeping in, I remember to take a minute and breath.

I also listen to life coaching material as this helps me see things from a different perspective.

Q: You sure have learnt a lot on your journey A! Anything else you would like to share before we wrap up?

A: We don't know what tomorrow will bring, but I look back on those dark times and almost feel grateful as it taught me so much. I feel proud that I came through it a better person, with so much love and respect for those around me.

I feel lucky and blessed to have them, and it's taught me positive and useful life lessons

I think we can choose how much stress to absorb, and my feeling is that I should focus on the positives and embrace the person that has come out the other side.

Q: Thank you A for your honesty in sharing your experience of stress.

I know many readers will be able to resonate with your story and they will draw strength from your experience. *(A from London)*

 One of the symptoms of an approaching nervous breakdown is the belief that one's work is terribly important."(Bertrand Russell)

Stress, work and burnouts

Living with Stress

I always considered myself resilient, until I realised I was burnt out from work stress. It creeps up so slowly, it's like a shadow that slowly insinuates itself into little bits of your life, and before long, you feel like that shadow is you.

I worked hard at my job; I really liked it. Interesting people, travel, it was stimulating. A week after I started, my line manager went off sick and never came back - I took on his workload. There always seemed to be more and more work, never keeping pace with what was going on in the department.

I worked long hours and took work home at weekends, always telling myself I would be on top of it then. But the following week was no different. I tried to talk to line managers, but all they kept telling me was how well I was doing, and my appraisals were always glowing.

I noticed I started to get palpitations when I arrived at work, I wasn't sleeping well, and my concentration was off. All I could think about was how tired I was. Then the final straw, I told my manager I wasn't coming in the next day; he said I'd be fine, just get on the train and go to the meeting. I didn't; I realised I had to get out now.

I never went back and went off sick. I tried to cope but eventually ended up on antidepressants. I found it incredibly difficult to talk to my very supportive husband and saw a psychiatrist a couple of times for reports; my husband said he wanted his wife back. I found it difficult to find joy in life.

It took several years for me to even think about doing something else. I've never got my resilience back and always feel I must manage what I do and not take on too much. That's what stress is like. It can build so slowly with you just coping until you get to a tipping point. But it never just affects you; it affected my husband and our relationship. *(J from the Channel Islands)*

Chapter 10

Stress, The Brain & The Science

By Laurence Nicholson

Let me start with the fact that I know my experience was at the intense end of the spectrum; however, you never know where your own experience will lie on that curve until after it is over. Always assuming it ever is over, which for me it never quite is.

What I am looking to share here with you is less about my actual experience, I have already published a book about that, but more of why I experienced what I did, the neuroscience, if you will, and what I discovered through a great deal of research and experimentation to give my brain, and yours, everything it needs to avoid it happening again.

Now, because I don't want you, the reader, to have to go and look up a whole bunch of terms and research papers, I will be endeavouring to keep it as near to layman's language as I can. After all, I want this to be a source of useful information and techniques, not another reference book.

I decided I would structure my piece into two distinct sections. Firstly, a description of the brain and the way stress impacts it, and I'm talking workplace stress as this is about burnout which is only driven from the workplace environment. And secondly, elements of the interplay between the two key parts of the brain, that highlight how we can use techniques, or 'hacks', to provide your brain with the conditions it needs to operate under peak conditions. There are inevitably crossovers and I will point them out where needed.

Let's get going with the first section: Neuronal Structure (don't panic! It's not in super detail) and Intelligence.

As a structure, our brains are incredible, having approximately 80 billion nerve cells, called neurones. That is more than ten times as many (in each brain) as there are people living on Earth.

As incomprehensible as that is, each of those single neurones may contain thousands of synapses, which are that small pocket of space between two cells where they can pass chemical messages to communicate.

In fact, one type of neurone called the Purkinje cell, found in the brain's cerebellum, is thought to have as many as one hundred thousand synapses, and there are approximately 125 trillion synapses, just in the cerebral cortex alone. That's roughly equal to the number of stars in 1,500 Milky Way Galaxies!

As we all realise, our brain is extremely complex in how it operates, but for the most part, I will focus on the two main protagonists in the reaction and management of stress, namely the limbic system (System 1) and the pre-frontal cortex (System 2).

When compared, if the pre-frontal cortex (PFC) can hold, say 256 GB of information (a typical capacity of a common memory card), then the limbic system can hold 2,500,000 GB (2.5 PB). To put that in perspective, 2.5 PB is the amount of storage it would take for us to record 10,000 digital photos every day for the average lifetime!

Through advances in neuroscience, there emerged not only limitations in capacity for the PFC, but also an age-based degeneration in one of the two types of intelligence our brains hold.

When we are young and are operating as the information sponges all children are, we are increasing the crystallised intelligence we store away, or the 'learned and experienced' knowledge.

This enters the large capacity limbic system (the 2.5 PB storage area) and is our store of knowledge we draw upon all through our lives. It holds much of the automatic pilot knowledge, like how to drive a car or ride a bicycle, for instance.

Our other type of intelligence, our 'Fluid' intelligence, represents our ability to 'consider' our immediate surroundings and situation, and apply relevant and pertinent situational information against previously learned and experienced knowledge, to determine the optimum solution for any current problem. Our problem-solving ability.

What we know is that as we age, our storage of new information flattens out after around 35 to 40 years of age and degrades once we are heading past 60 to 65. This is not a huge issue, as it means we keep much of what we learn over our lifetime as crystallised intelligence; however, our 'Fluid' intelligence, the problem-solving part, tends to peak around our 20's and begins to decline, increasing its rate at around the age of 40, on average.

This has been thought to be a contributor to forms of memory degradation, dementia and Alzheimer's Disease, where the memories are still stored, but the ability to access them is diminished.

So what is the 'Hack' for lengthening our access to our 'learned and experienced' intelligence? Actually, it has been found that continued 'exercising' of the appropriate cognitive skills through regular use of cognitive exercises, like those on Apps or old-fashioned books/cards, can delay the onset of decline, and reduce the gradient, meaning we get to remember and apply our knowledge for longer.

Phew! That's the first one over. Now for the next section: Your Pre-Frontal Cortex (PFC) and its limitations.

We touched on the capacity limitations of the PFC in the last section, and introduced the fact that it gets tired very quickly because of the high effort and limited energy available. It is because of the resource needs that this part of the brain is often lazy and indecisive, trying to preserve energy in case of emergency.

In fact, your PFC is the newest part of your brain, developed to operate within the expansion of our complex socio-cultural environment, to handle language, complex executive functioning and decision making, amongst other things. It actually makes up some 80% of the brain by weight, covering the brain as a form of mesh or gauze and is the grey 'wormy' matter under the cranium. Part of its function is to regulate the levels of key chemicals, nor-epinephrine and dopamine, vital in the communication processes between neurons.

Strategic in our processing of external inputs like sight, smell, touch and hearing, it actually receives 90% of its information input from internal neural processing, in the form of body, memory and emotion scanning, in order to recognise and associate neuronal maps of previous experiences to the current situation.

All of what we see as 'considered' decision making, or problem-solving, is pretty much dependent on the PFC, as it processes all the information we are exposed to at any given moment, and uses this to recall billions of associated maps from our existing knowledge, to let us create new and novel solutions to current problems. All of this uses a large amount of effort and, whilst logical, is extremely slow when compared to the reactionary limbic system, and therefore cannot be sustained for a prolonged period.

In contrast, the limbic system, also called the reptilian brain, is the oldest part, and has had a significantly longer development period and is thus far more efficient.

This area is our 'automatic pilot' and is where our survival reactions are managed, with the sub-cortical structures of the hippocampus, hypothalamus and amygdala involved in memory and emotion. It is fast, associative and unconscious in our awareness. Once the PFC is tired and loses its regulation function, increases in norepinephrine and dopamine alter the chemical communication pathways between neurones and our ways of decision-making change, leading to compulsive behaviours and emotional responses.

It is clear we need to keep the PFC operating at its optimum level, with sufficient energy to maintain its regulatory function, so how can we do that?

Well, we need to focus on three key areas. Impulse control, attention and selective attention, and arousal control.

Impulse control is the exercise of constraint from automatic, emotive reaction or immediate gratification. Practising 'self-control' of your emotions affects your Impulse control and therefore your decision making, reducing reactive behaviour that results in rapid unconsidered decisions. And we can do this using the Stroop task and the Transcription task, found in many brain training apps, designed to manipulate self-control strength.

Attention next, and it is a slippery character, despite people thinking it is simple.

"Surely you are either 'present' (paying attention), or you are not, right?"

Not really.

You see, attention is the sweet spot where we have optimum balance between access and use of the limbic system and our learned and experienced knowledge, and PFC control over our focus on the present information from all our inputs. This is highly energy hungry and exceptionally fragile.

For dealing with complex problems, we need to be selectively focused too, bringing all our cognitive powers to a single focal point. 'Single-tasking' if you like. To do this, we need to avoid all interruptions, especially as a study at UCAL found that, on average, each disruption added some 25 minutes of total refocus time to a task.

So, how do we exercise our attention and selective attention skills? We use exercises like 'quick counts' and 'memory journeys' to focus attention, and 'tricky colours' and 'shape shuffles' to select specific elements of that attention group to drill in on.

Now all of this is great, but if your cognitive state is either under or over aroused, you will be unable to maintain, or even achieve, a peak level of performance.

Now, we have all experienced situations when we have not been in the best emotional state for an impending event or activity; be it lethargy first thing in the morning or towards the end of the day, or over excitement or anxiety when heading to an important event or meeting. This can find us struggling to be 'present' or to maintain a clear thought process under pressure.

We need to find the point where our arousal, emotional and cognitive, is at the peak area of the arousal graph, like a Goldilocks spot. Not too much and not too little, but just right.

Luckily, we can use techniques to help us do this, and in fact, we see them all the time in top-flight sport. We see Olympic swimmers using calming techniques of listening to music or meditating immediately before a race, and who hasn't seen the aggressive slapping and hitting of a power-lifter's coach just before they go out for a heavy lift?

Of course, we don't need to go to such extremes, but we can take cues from them. If we find ourselves under aroused and lethargic, rapid breathing exercises, physical exertion and even caffeine, lifts the arousal out of the depths.

If, on the other hand, we find we are panicking and feeling anxiety over an impending meeting, situation or interview, a simple walk outside, a quick meditation, or use of the 4-7-8 breathing system (4 seconds in, hold for 7, and release over 8 seconds) repeated as much as necessary, will trigger our parasympathetic nervous system to lower heart rate and relax various muscles and bodily functions to bring down our stress and anxiety.

Obviously, in this single chapter, I have just scratched the surface of the complexities of our brain and how it is affected by pressures and stressors from the workplace and life in general. There is much more to know and understand, which is covered at the deeper levels of my Masterclasses, but the first step is just to be aware of the two 'systems' of our PFC and limbic areas, what they generally are best at, and what elements we should focus on, and apply the suggestions given, in order to prevent the exhaustion of those critical brain areas which regulate our behaviour, performance and decision logic, which ultimately leads to significant impacts to lives if left unchecked.

Contact: Laurence Nicholson:

Founder and CEO the N Cubed Group and

burnouthacker.com,

Global-Award Winning Proactive Burnout Educator,

Certified Corporate Mental Health Facilitator,

Certified Corporate Wellness Coach, Author, Speaker,

Regular Trustee,

Civil & Commercial Mediator, Counsellor, Paralegal and

Former Corporate Change Agent & Managing Consultant.

Physical Environment, Food for Thought

EMF and dirty electricity

Modern life and the way we live nowadays has electronic devices woven into all parts of our life. From smartphones to doorbells, we are surrounded by electronic devices.

Statistics from 2018 estimate 22 Billion devices being connected around the world, and fifty billion are estimated for 2030.

A study from 2022 shows that 90% of data was created in the last two years alone, and 5G is estimated to be 100 times faster than 4G.

Compare this to 1984 when only 8.2% of people owned a computer.

This is a staggering increase, and I am certain it is not going to stop there.

EMFs exist in the natural world, the sun, the earth, our bodies, all produce them as we are made up of atoms, electricity, energy. We are EMFs.

However, man-made devices are different as their electromagnetic frequencies disrupt our natural one, causing a low-level undetectable level of stress on a cellular level, triggering symptoms in our body.

Our nervous system and cell structures get disrupted by that high input of EMFs.

Those who are particularly sensitive will suffer more symptoms to the point where they cannot cope.

My Personal Experience

I wish I had known then what I know now
I first started using computers when studying again in 2001. Working long hours on the computer threw up a host of unpleasant symptoms like tingling feeling in my hands when typing, brain fog and hissing in my ears, my stiff neck was probably more due to bad posture, to be honest.

Researching the effects of EMFs on the body, the findings in those days were inconclusive, however still worrying enough for me to keep an eye on further developments.

Four years later we moved house and could not get a good night's sleep; for the first year, we would be wide awake until the early hours, living our life wired and tired; that's when I found out about dirty electricity, the hard way, I might add. I'd wander around the house putting my hands on the walls, at times feeling a gentle sizzling, similar to the one when working on the computer, sometimes it was more like mini electric shocks.

When we finally called an electrician, the findings were shocking (pardon the pun):

Live uninsulated wires had been left in the walls under the new plaster.

Needless to say, we had the whole house rewired. Never had a sleepless night again.

Hence, I am including some of the results of my ongoing research for your consideration.

The jury is out on how damaging EMFs are; however, I suggest you read up on the subject and enable yourself to make an educated decision.

Signs and symptoms
- tiredness
- buzzing in ears and head
- sudden loss of hearing / tinnitus

- mood swings
- forgetfulness
- sinusitis
- dizziness
- nose bleeds
- visual disturbances
- joint and limb pain
- night sweats
- nausea
- sleeplessness

Things to try

- EMF shielding devices, including specialised wall paints
- Remove EMF devices from your bedrooms
- Switch electronic devices off at the mains.
- Restrict your time on electronic devices, balance with time out in nature
- Use a grounding mat when working
- Barefoot walking to load your body with negative ions
- Plants around your computer
- Shungite stones: they have a unique carbon structure which enables them to both absorb and reflect EMF frequencies. They have been researched and patented by the Russian Federation and the United States.

- Herbs taken internally or smelled as an essential oil, particularly fennel, mint, and lemonbalm will help to calm your nervous system.

The extra stress factor: Toxins in your environment

Unfortunately, we are surrounded by an increasing load of toxins which are in nearly every item we use, eat or have around the house, from heavy metals (lead, mercury, cadmium) to BPAs in modern plastic packaging, tin linings, plastic bottles and even paper receipts.

VCOs off-gassing from paints and new furniture, carpets and clothes (those we can actually smell, so keep your rooms well ventilated). TBT and PFOAs leached into our ground and water are toxic to our wildlife, and disrupt our hormone balance, thus increasing stressors in the body.

Today's creams, shampoos, cleaning products, vinyls, kids' toys, and plastic packaging, our world is full of toxins which we absorb through the skin, breathe, eat in our food and drink in our water.

Look into
- Specific air purifiers/extractors
- toxin absorbent/VCO-free organic paints
- fresh, unadulterated food
- water filters
- simple cleaning products like vinegar, and bicarbonate of soda
- use essential oils instead of room fragrances / perfumes

- check what is in your creams and deodorants; check your food for additives, artificial colours and tastes.

Reducing the amount of detox work your body has to do, gives your body more energy to deal with other stressors in your life.

Mycotoxins

They need a special mention as they exist in nearly every house. They are released by mould and spread everywhere via spores. As an opportunistic invader, it can spread everywhere in damp environments, particularly bathrooms and kitchens and around windows. Toxic to your body, they cause irritations, skin rashes, and breathing problems, to mention but a few.

Food and houseplants can carry the spores, settling where they can grow, including inside your body.

SECTION FOUR

Stress, our Modern World, and Finding Balance

 Future medicine will be the medicine of frequencies"

(Albert Einstein)

VISIONARY APPROACHES AND REAL-LIFE SOLUTIONS

Chapter 11

Be the Change you want to see in the World!
By Beverly Radley

A combination of six essences to bring understanding and change to your SELF.

Stressed!!

That blind panic where you can't think straight and don't know what you need? It feels like you are on the hamster wheel of life, and if you stop at any moment, you will fall off!

Would you like to learn to connect with yourself, listen, tune into your feelings and act on what you need?

In 1930 physician Edward Bach sought support for his emotions and turned to nature. He discovered that everything has a frequency, and by using vibrational medicine, you can change your frequency. The very essence of nature helped him.

connect with the essence of himself. Using his techniques, I have produced a sequence of essences that help connect deeply into who you are and to your own essence, which is often hidden under piles of shoulds, coulds, need to, and old, outdated beliefs which are often not even your own.

So how do you connect more deeply with yourself and unpeel the onion layers hiding your true self?

Let's look at the impact of stress and how essences can help.

Stress can be caused by many things, but the impact and result is being out of alignment.

The journey of knowing and connecting to your true self involves you releasing anything inharmonious in your body, banishing outdated aspects and opening up to new ways of being.

Vibrational essences are a natural way of helping to bring you into the alignment you need. I have co-created The Breakthrough and Reconnect Range, a set of six essences designed to facilitate bringing harmony to modern-day living. They will help you reconnect to your SELF, and it is by connecting to the SELF that we learn, grow, and deepen our understanding.

These are six aspects of the SELF-
1. SELF-care

2. SELF-love

3. SELF-expression

4. SELF-understanding

5. SELF-compassion

6. SELF-worth,

Modern, western society has praised busyness, and aspects of it, such as multitasking, so you sometimes need to give yourself permission to stop! The first essence does exactly that:

1. REST AND RESTORE ESSENCE - SELF-care
Stop Pushing: Recoup: Nourish Yourself

With white chestnut to calm a busy mind, this essence helps with the "being busy, being busy" spiral that prevents you from seeing and feeling what you need, and gives yourSELF permission to pause and rest. Rest can be beneficial. Sometimes all you need is a few minutes when you truly connect to how you are feeling and notice what your "busy" is trying to communicate to you. Those few minutes can be enough to check in and see what is needed.

SELF-care can be hijacked by commercialism. Ask yourself the simple yet profound question: "What is it I need?"

You don't have to drink green tea and do yoga if it's not your thing! Pause and take time to see what you do like. Do you really know? It might be that what you used to like has changed, so try new things too.

Write down five things that bring you joy when you pause… these could involve music, peacefulness, movement, tea, nature or even fresh bed sheets.

- 1
- 2
- 3
- 4
- 5

When you are stressed, you can easily forget what you need.

When you have them already written down, you can choose one from the list to help.

In the process of stopping, we see what is happening. Often, we are aware we have many hot rocks taken from others, or have ambitiously gifted them to ourselves! Are you holding on and feeling weighed down by them?

This next combination can help.

2. "LET GO AND RECEIVE" ESSENCE – SELF-love

Reach Out: Allow Assistance: Accept

Allow yourself to acknowledge things, to release tears of sadness, to notice if you are exhausted. Olive essence helps with exhaustion and is blended with the Ray of Hope essence to acknowledge where you are and to bring in light, and then you can start to make changes. In each combination, there is support for what is challenging you - help with fear and moving with change, as well as a higher frequency of Unconditional Love to move you to change. Your innate being knows what is needed. As you shift your frequency and start to match the higher vibration of the essence, things start to shift energetically in you. Others often see this in you before you see it in yourself.

Can you list three things to release?

- 1
- 2
- 3

3. CONNECT TO SELF ESSENCE - SELF-expression

Reflect: Connect: Surrender

When SELF-expression is ignored and overridden, it can often come out as a burst of emotions which have been suppressed and ignored for so long. You are a mind, a soul and an emotional being. The whole of you works best when you are seamlessly connected to all aspects of yourSELF. When you get stressed or busy, do you disconnect from being present, override your need for food, thirst, ignore the toilet until you are bursting?

This essence helps to ground you and keep you present. When you are more present, you are more aware of your needs and can better express yourself. It helps prevent low self-esteem, over-giving and putting your own needs last. Now you can learn to fully express what you need, so you can feel and understand before changing the way you allow others to treat you.

How do you …
- Connect …
- Express…
- Reflect…

4. INNER WORK ESSENCE – SELF-understanding
Release Criticism: Love Yourself: Discover Your Light

Now let's reflect on your lineage and inherited beliefs. What patterns of behaviour do you do by habit or subconsciously? What a gift to give yourself - the time to reflect on what to take forward and which ancestral patterns to release.

By releasing the harsh critic and facilitating you to discover your own alignment, the Time to Align essence encourages change in your life from a deep place of love and understanding of your true self.

How would you benefit if you released self-criticism?

- I am…
- I feel …
- I have…

5. HARMONY AND BALANCE ESSENCE – SELF-COMPASSION

Clarity: Purpose: Energy

What needs to change? Fireweed can help release your outdated beliefs, and Time to Shine allows you to connect with your inner light and intuition, trusting and allowing you to be more compassionate with yourself. YOU matter, and innately you know what you need to bring harmony into your world. This helps you learn to eliminate things that drain you and allows you to live a life aligned with your true purpose.

My purpose is to…

- 1
- 2
- 3

6. BE THE CHANGE ESSENCE – SELF-worth

Intuition: Oneness: Destiny

Things can get over complicated, and life can get so hectic; this experience of being in human form is LIFE. There is only one you. Nobody else is you! What a unique position to be in, knowing that you being here on earth and just being is enough! But you need direction and purpose; allow your intuition and destiny to bring forward the unique gifts that only you can share with this world.

This essence allows you to release the lower energies of not respecting and valuing yourself so you can learn to love yourself unconditionally, not because you're good at something, how you look or what you own – this embraces an acceptance of every aspect of you UNCONDITIONALLY!

Simply using this essence alone has a profound effect on your being. Wild Oat essence helps you connect with your life direction and purpose, with the confidence to get out into the world and be passionate about who you are and your destiny.

I am passionate about …

- 1
- 2
- 3

These six essences can be taken in order to alleviate your stress. However, as a self-empowerment tool, they allow you to go so much deeper. As you work with the essences to connect and release aspects of yourself and discover new areas of understanding, you gift yourself time to reflect, think about, and connect to your true self.

Did you fill in the questions?

What have you discovered about yourself?

Want to go a step further? The essences, affirmation cards and journal can strengthen your discovery even further.

This process is a journey where you connect and know what you need to flourish from misalignment; it takes you to who you choose to be in your true magnificence.

How should the essences be taken?
Simply add 4-6 drops of the combination you have chosen to your water bottle. This allows your body to receive gentle reminders throughout the day as you sip, nurturing yourself, and aligning yourself to the new vibrational frequency.

Or add the combination of your choice to your bath; this allows you to release or connect to the frequency you need.

As Albert Einstein stated:

"Future medicine will be the medicine of frequencies"

This protocol empowers you to make choices, to hear yourself and connect on a deeper level to who and what you need to be. As you change the frequency of your being, you become aware of how you are feeling and can align yourself more easily. You have an action to support yourself to make lasting change. As you step on the path of essences, the way opens up before you to destinations you perhaps had never thought of: Welcome to the Breakthrough and Reconnect journey and taking your first drops!

There is so much more to learn about essences - this is simply an introduction to the Breakthrough and Reconnect range that can bring about profound change. I would love to connect with you and support your journey. If you are drawn to these essences, do please get in touch.

Contact: Beverly Radley

Breakthrough From Within

Email - bevradley@gmail.com

www.breakthroughfromwithin.co.uk

https://etsy.me/2IP98ly

Find me on Facebook and Instagram "Breakthrough from within"

Let's "BE THE CHANGE YOU WANT TO SEE IN THE WORLD!"

INTERVIEW

Finding Life Balance

Q: Hello O; thank you for agreeing to this interview about stress and your personal experience with it.

We actually go way back, and when we first met in 2003 in our Naturopathic Nutritional Therapy training, we clicked over us both suffering from Eczema; I also remember you had other health issues too.

O: Hi, yes, I wasn't very well. I was suffering from emotional stress, eczema all over plus depression, which I didn't realise back then.

Q: Can you pinpoint a time when stress started for you?

O: Yes, this goes back to when I was 12/13 years old and suffered great emotional loss. The stress didn't really come out until later in life. My body held on to it for a long time, and I believe it festered inside me until it could not take anymore; it externalised as eczema and food allergies/sensitivity.

Q: What have you tried to make it better?

O: Over the years, the doctors have only tried to stop the symptoms. I have been on heavy doses of cortisone steroids, creams, immune-suppressing drugs and other things. None of which really helped.

I had to help myself by looking elsewhere and looking inside me as a person. Very scary really.

I enjoy food and am a chef, so I decided to see how food affects us and if one can heal with food.

Doing the Naturopath Nutrition course gave me an insight into the deeper workings of the body and the effects of nutrition on it. I started understanding the chemical reactions and how food can work with or against the body.

Q: So your stress manifested in eczema and eating right brought some relief, but I guess there was more going on?
O: Yes, I worked in hotels as a chef, without care for myself, smoked, and drank lots of coffee and alcohol. Looking back, I had no love for myself, abusing my body and slowly draining everything out of it. This just added to the emotional turmoil I was already feeling. Being alone and with no one really to lean on, I had to keep strong and carry on. With our busy lifestyles, there is no time to stop and think; pushing on is detrimental to one's mental, emotional and physical health. I had two mental breakdowns in life.

I was overdoing things, not knowing when to stop; as a "yes person", I was pushing myself, not allowing rest and recovery for my body to rebuild its defences and mend properly.

Q: So how did you change your life around?

O: My time in London came to a natural end when I was made redundant; as luck would have it, I had been diving down in Portland and was offered a job there; after ten years, I'm still here and very happily married too.

Learning to dive gave me a reason to take time out; going on a holiday was a novelty for me. Diving brought calmness; being in the water means there is only water needing your attention, you float effortlessly through this substance with wondrous animals living in it. All you have to think about is nothing. The world disappears.

It gave me a break, it re-centred me, I had a better work attitude and more vigour. It became a necessity to be in the cold water, to feel something that was real; it was like a lifeline.

Q: So cold water swimming is one of your strategies to deal with stress?

O: Yes, I've been doing this for over twenty years now. It became a sanctuary for me, a space where nothing else mattered; thoughts disappeared, worries, anxieties all went. It is invigorating. For a few moments a day, there is just the water and me.

Q: Thinking of now, what makes a real difference to your wellbeing

O: Apart from diving and cold-water swimming, the total change of my lifestyle.

I have changed; I live in a healthier place, changed my food, changed my habits. I am still a yes person and am still learning about myself, but I realise I have to be kind to me; diving, (cold water) swimming, brings me peace, it invigorates the body,

it brings life and energy. I have a positive outlook because I feel better. I don't really get sick now; my mental and emotional state has improved as I understand where it came from.

I still have good and bad days like everyone, but I try to make a conscious effort to be positive and look ahead. Being able to jump in the water when it's raining, the skies are dark, and the seas are moving, that's amazing. Having the rain beat on your back as you float, feeling the moment and the wonder of mother nature. And swimming into or against the waves, wondering, "Am I nuts?"

Embracing the dark and the light for what it is and finding the balance. *(O from Portland UK)*

Chapter 12

Tapping into the 'S' Word!

By Ramona Stronach

How did we get so 's' d out?!

We live in a time-space on earth where we have everything we could possibly want, conveniently. Yet so many of us hold stress in our bodies and energy fields on a continual basis that we are not aware of how stressed we are. Stress experienced in this way is definitely not natural for humans, yet it has become normalised in modern life.

When we give ourselves time to reflect upon the design (nothing is a coincidence) of the systems and structures we find ourselves living within, we start to see connections to our stress levels. We cannot talk about stress without reference to these systems because they have become so integral to our lives.

The majority of us are following someone else's agenda, rarely our own, despite common thinking that we are autonomous.

Consider the work system. The rush to get to work on time to avoid punitive consequences.

Or the policies that dictate we can have a set amount of days to grieve for the loss of loved ones. Whilst not overtly stressful like the experience of losing a loved one, it all creates background stress in our daily lives.

How can we forget about that tension and anxiety in the build-up to Monday morning unless we love and feel connected to the work we have chosen to do? Even with annual leave – usually a race to get the best pick of the days – so many of us experience feeling run down because our body is so relieved to release the stress now that we are finally resting!

Stress from the digital systems is not obvious, but step back from it, and you realise you are a slave to its systems. The media is designed to invoke fear which puts the body immediately into stress. Even the television, whilst it appears innocent, also causes stress within our bodies.

Look at how in our society and culture we hand responsibility for our children's learning over to nursery and school, and when we see them at the end of these routines, we are so tired and stressed out because most of us are working to meet the demands of keeping our homes that the banking system threatens to take away if we don't keep up the payments.

Is this why we came to beautiful planet earth to experience?

Wouldn't you think that with all the wonderful technological advances we should have more time and freedom to enjoy our lives, experience optimal health, and live into what is really important to us?

The above are just a few examples (so much more can be explored) of how the external world creates a never-ending wheel for us that creates conflict and stress within, and can prevent us from being attuned to our deepest values and looking at what is truly important in our lives. Whilst the constructs we live within bring us some quality of life (for those who can access them), the question is, at what cost to our body, mind and spirit?

When stressed, we simply do not have the energy to consider these critical questions, and many more, about life; what do happiness and joy mean to us as individuals and as communities?

How can we live in more natural and wholesome ways?

How can we have harmonious relationships?

How can we return to respectful ways of living to honour nature that we are deeply connected to, yet our cities have been created without great reverence to this fact?

When we really analyse our external world rather than accepting it's 'just this way,' we begin to wake up our consciousness as we start to see through the beliefs that construct it. Beliefs that do not always serve us and, therefore humanity.

Aside from the destructive nature of stress to our physical, mental and emotional health, if left unchecked, stress depletes us of creative energy – not only of the artistic kind.

Our creative energy enables us to resolve situations in balanced and healthy ways. It is this place of creative energy that inspires us to take action that feels light and 'in flow' for us, that our wisdom thoughts can arise. This expansive energy makes us feel into our aliveness, and we thrive!

Creative energy enables us to think critically and feel into the truth of a matter - both on the internal and external levels - and never before has this been more crucial for the direction of humanity now.

We tune more into our consciousness and are better placed to more easily choose positive thoughts that serve us rather than recycling negative thoughts that do not. It is the energy that lets us step into our heart's desires; to move towards our true and deepest vision for our lives.

In stress mode – of which fear is the baseline – creative energy does not have a chance to emerge because the body is not in homeostasis (the optimal state for the body to be in). The mind is in overdrive; our energy is conserved for fight or flight action, and we find ourselves living from a reactive place, and life can become automatic for us. We are in danger of being controlled by the external world and cutting ourselves off from our true power and potential.

Reaction mode is not a natural way to be unless you need to move away from danger! Aside from the potential of harming our relationships, we are disconnecting from our true self. We cannot tune into the governance of ourselves, living to our own truth and making choices that support our deepest values - true autonomy. This, I believe, is the spirit and essence of being human that we need to celebrate!

The stressful self is not our real Self. It does not define us - although, in the moment of feeling stress, we can feel like we are totally consumed by it.

We cannot see beyond it, just as we cannot see beyond the systems and structures that can keep our energies contracted if we are predominantly in this state of being.

In my workshops, I teach how tapping (Emotional Freedom Technique) interrupts the energy of stress and connects us to the present moment again. It brings us back into our bodies and out of our minds, and we can direct our minds to serve us rather than take us over. This is because the technique calms the primal mechanism in our brain that puts our natural physiological response to threat into action. Broadly speaking, it is the continual re-activation of this mechanism from the external world's systems that is the 'danger' our subconscious mind cannot perceive the difference between being penalised for having too much sick leave from an oppressive work system, or a threat to our life.

Connection to our bodies is critical if we are to live into our amazing potential. The myriad of subtle energies within us that let us know something is not right, are easily missed if our attention is focused continuously on the external world. Unfortunately, the modern world has done a good job at disconnecting us from the Divine intelligence of our bodies.

In tapping, we honour what we feel, thereby acknowledging the energy within our body, whilst the tapping action enables energy to move through our body system.

From this place, we begin to access our consciousness beyond the stressful self.

We can focus more easily on the outcome we would like to experience from any situation once we release the intensity from the stress we feel or, indeed, any other challenges we face in life.

We also begin to perceive situations, events, and people – i.e. (external triggers) – differently because we remove the layers of conditioning and beliefs. Emotional intensity is discharged, and we find that with regular tapping, we naturally begin to move towards responding rather than reacting ways of being.

Remember that creative energy which is overridden by stress most of the time? We can tap into this and use our power of consciousness to serve us in better ways. As a Matrix Re-imprinting* Practitioner, I guide clients to communicate with their past (and future) consciousness (this is known as an ECHO, an energetic consciousness hologram that holds information in memories) to seek resolution in unresolved memories and create new better serving beliefs in their subconscious mind resulting in positive life experiences.

With both of these powerful tools, we can access our wisdom and begin to consciously engage with the external world rather than let systems and negative beliefs underpinning so much of our world keep us stressed and in automatic and reactionary ways of being. And this is just one aspect of tapping!

Contact: Ramona Stronach

Email: ramona@tapyourpossible.com

Mobile: 07436903244

 "If you want to find the secrets of the universe, think in terms of Energy Frequency and vibration" (Nikola Tesla)

HSPs (Highly Sensitive People)

There is more than meets the eye.

HSP first gained recognition in the early 90s when Elaine Aron started her research on the subject.

As an HSP myself, I can certainly emphasise with how difficult and confusing it can be.

It took me years to figure out what was "wrong" with me and why I would repeatedly hear "you are different."

In my 40is I finally figured out what was going on, and finally started to understand that I indeed perceived things differently and therefore could not assume that others saw and felt the same things I did.

For HSPs, there is just so much more going on than meets the eye.

Sensitives perceive the world around them with more intensity and detail, almost as if there are more sensors present.

We pick up vibes from people, nature, buildings, thoughts and much more, and distinguishing between what is us versus what is "other" can prove to be tricky.

This can easily lead to overstimulation; things can become too intense, our brain has to process so much more, which easily leads to an overstimulated stress response.

As HSPs, we have to learn to withdraw within ourselves to access a safe zone, and will need downtime to process the myriad of sensory information.

If you suspect you might be an HSP, I can highly recommend reading Elaine Aron's books and checking out her website or getting in touch with me.

 Our beginnings, the past, and the future.

"To take back control over our nervous system, our body, mind and emotions, we need to look at what happened in the beginning of ourselves."

It is important to acknowledge our own birth and early childhood imprinting on our nervous system.

This is not to throw blame on anybody but to highlight that the time of gestation in the womb and the manner of our birth, like our childhood, also imprint on our nervous system. As always, knowledge is power, power to release the unwanted, letting it go and moving on, no blame attached.

Chapter 13

The Magical World of Energetic Healing
By Su Winsbury

The stress response is a beautifully designed work of art, a feat of chemical engineering to be admired and respected.

It enables the body to react and respond with clarity, energy, focus and an automatic shutdown of all the processes not needed in the given moment of alert, danger or fear.

Sadly, as we all know, we now rarely use this incredible response in the way in which it was originally designed, and for the vast majority of the population, we stay stuck in various degrees of constant stress, unable to switch off or give our bodies the time to recalibrate, rebalance and settle back into the rest or digest phase.

Having worked with the human body from a holistic and energetic perspective for many years, I see stress as the root cause of a multitude of physical and emotional issues. And one of my most insightful observations has been how great an impact our birth has on our ability to manage stress from the very first breath we take.

I have witnessed this with one of my sons, who, by the age of 22, was burnt out and unable to manage normal daily activities. His frenetic A-type lifestyle wasn't sustainable, but it is only on looking deeper into what prompted him to behave the way he did, into his thought and belief structures and his constant drive to achieve, that I began to unravel the story back to his birth.

His arrival into the world was long, difficult, and ultimately his survival was in question. By the time he was unceremoniously unzipped from my belly, we were both exhausted and traumatised. Except I had no concept that he might be traumatised, and neither was it something the medical profession ever acknowledged or mentioned at the time. What became evident in later years was that from that point on, his fragile nervous system had no idea how to switch off. It was already stuck in high alert, believing that this world was a dangerous place and that life itself was fraught with danger from the outset.

None of that was obvious.

Birth trauma from the baby's emotional and nervous system perspective didn't enter my mind and certainly wasn't mentioned by anyone in the medical profession at the time.

And I didn't know then what I know now.

The chemical make-up of the body is so refined and delicate that it can be easily unbalanced, resulting in all kinds of ailments, issues and disease.

Many of the clients I have worked with who have long-term health issues – particularly those that have long-term fatigue related conditions – have experienced a difficult birth, or even pre-birth trauma. I have found it fascinating investigating this from an interest perspective (as opposed to clinical research).

Cords around the neck, inductions, emergency sections and the like will place the baby into a natural stress response; that is how the body is designed. However, very often, that trauma is never recognised or dealt with. It becomes embedded in the subconscious, creating beliefs and vortexes of trapped energy within the body system whilst also often triggering a constant allegiance with the sympathetic nervous system, the fight or flight response system.

And this is not to say I am advocating planned Caesareans as a means to avoiding such issues. Natural delivery carries with it so many benefits – again, the body is designed well and should be given every opportunity to perform as nature, or the Divine Creator, intended.

This early developmental impact can even be tracked back to those whose mothers may have experienced frequent stress whilst the baby is in the womb. The emotions, beliefs, and stress responses all flow into the baby energetically, if not biologically.

At this point, if you are a mother who experienced a stressful time whilst pregnant or during childbirth, please do not start beating yourself up and blaming yourself or anyone else for any impact you may or may not have created.

Life happens.
Shit happens.
To.
Us.
All.

There is no point in suddenly burdening yourself with regrets, guilt, shame, blame or any other negative emotions. It's too late, and it won't change anything. The greatest gift right now would be forgiveness – to yourself and anyone else involved.

The most powerful way to deal with this kind of experience or trauma is through recognition, healing and deep energy work.

Energetically we are capable of healing so much, especially all that is hidden deep within our internal layers.

We are comprised of the physical body and an energetic body, and much of what is stored in our subconscious is held within this energy body of ours.

And the joy of the human body means that we can also shift things energetically.

Energy moves in three ways. It can either be in flow – those times when everything feels aligned, easy and marvellous. It can be in resistance – these are the days when it feels like everything is hard work; you are swimming against the tide but still getting where you need to be, albeit slowly and arduously. Or it can be in reversal when it stops in its tracks, unable to move and stuck in time.

Trauma (with a big T or a little t) often creates reversals which then remain stuck in the energy body like blobs of grey heavy matter, getting in the way of everything else and clogging up the system.

The conscious mind is unable to detect these; they are often buried way too deep and simply not available to the physical mind or memory. It is a rare being indeed who can remember first-hand what they experienced in the womb, or during the journey down the birth canal, or in their moment of expulsion out into the real world.

As a coach, I know that no amount of coaching, counselling or talking therapy can access these recesses.

But energy healing modalities can and do. With infinite ease and simplicity.

Having trained in several different methods, there is true power and magic in working with the energetic body. Whilst the mind might not remember, the energy body does, and through communicating with the energy, it becomes a relatively simple process to uncover the root cause of an issue.

I remember working with one client who had long-term fatigue issues. As we worked with her energy, we were led back to her birth as being a traumatic experience.

She had been a ventouse baby, and as we worked on releasing the experience from her subconscious, she could literally feel the suction cap pulling at the top of her head as we let go of the energetic memory. Within weeks her physical energy had recovered to a level that she hadn't known for many years.

Similarly, another client was born with the umbilical cord around his neck, meaning he entered the world in a high state of fear and alert. By his mid-forties, he had struggled with fatigue related issues since his teenage years. There is never just one thing that causes long-term fatigue conditions, it is always a layering of multiple contributory factors, however, being able to track back to the earliest stress response can help unravel the complex and subtle behaviours and responses. Working energetically, this client could feel tightness around his throat as we disseminated the energy, beliefs and emotions connected to his birth.

Working with energy doesn't always lead back to birth of course. We all experience many challenging situations and have different responses – what one person might embed as a traumatic experience, another may process differently.

What does traverse these experiences is the power of healing through energy.

B had experienced neck pain for many years when she came to see me. By working with her energy, we were guided back to the point in her teens where she had become aware of her father's dependency on alcohol. This was the unconscious trigger for her neck pain; the situation quite literally was a pain in the neck to her emotionally, physically and energetically. We were able to release the resonance of that memory together with a host of other emotions until she actually reached a place of forgiveness and peace in her heart. The neck pain disappeared. And she also felt the presence of her long-since departed dad wrapping her in love.

Mr O, a big burly ex-policeman, could barely contain his eye roll when I explained that we needed to work energetically with his issue rather than coaching.

To say he was cynical would be an understatement.

However, to give him credit, he was open to giving it a try. Within 15 minutes, we had tapped into his 7-year-old self; he had tears rolling down his face as we conversed with this inner child and allowed that child to heal. He left the session eternally grateful with the words, "I don't know what you have done to me, but that was incredible".

The truth is, I didn't do anything. He did the work, I just facilitated him accessing what he needed.

Such is the wonder and magic of energetic healing.

The modalities I use are EAM (Energy Alignment Method), EFT (Emotional Freedom Technique), Inner Child Work and

Conscious Journeys, all accompanied by a deep sense of intuitive guidance. There are many other methods available.

We all have this potential within.
We can all create magical changes and shifts, it is just a matter of finding the right way for you and being guided and supported by a practitioner who knows how to do this kind of work with absolute integrity and the highest of principles.

So, journeying back to stress, no matter what has happened, whether it is in your conscious awareness or deeply submerged, we all have the ability to peel back the layers, unearth the origins and heal.

The more we let go of stress, the more the body is able to function in the way it has been created, in a place of harmony, natural equilibrium and flow. It truly is the most incredible creation, so finely tuned and balanced, we owe it to this physical home to do all we can to support it so that it can continue supporting us.

Contact: Su Winsbury:

Spiritual Mentor, Wellbeing & Empowerment Coach &

Burnout Recovery Specialist

Contact details:

www.suwinsbury.com

Email: su@suwinsbury.com

Summary

How to step into the future

I have no doubt that our current world, and the way we live, has introduced new stressors into our day-to-day living which we have not yet adjusted to; however, over time, we will.

New generations will have developed different responses with an adapted nervous system able to deal with EMFs, toxins, and so much more we can't yet even imagine.

At the same time, with the strong emergence of new science and research, we now understand that we can adapt consciously and don't have to leave it up to chance.

So what does that mean for us humans at this time, this our own lifetime?

It means we don't have to suffer it; we can become proactive, taking action.

None of us can predict the future; however, we can learn how to deal with events without letting the stress response overwhelm us, and we can learn to change our reactions.

The more knowledge and understanding we have about ourselves, our environment and the people around us, the better we will become in dealing with our inner and outer stressors.

By balancing out negative impacts from our surroundings and our own thoughts and emotions, by embracing new methods and incorporating helpful new habits in our daily lives, we can achieve balance instead of derailing our nervous system, plunging us into stress and a downward spiral of ill health.

Keeping the balance is key.

This book was created to provide you with insights, tools and methods of how to keep yourself and your life in balance. You will also find a host of further useful resources and a reading list, which I hope proves helpful to you.

Wishing you a joyful, balanced life, aligned in the present where the past is just that and the future something to look forward to.

With gratitude, love & light

Andrea Ursula Hochgatterer

N.B.

If you have any concerns about your health and are struggling with your stress responses, please get in touch with your healthcare provider.

If you want to discuss any of the topics covered in this book please don't hesitate to get in touch.

About the Creator

Andrea Ursula Hochgatterer
RCST, RNT, Dip CNM, Dip CCST

Andrea was born in Austria and moved to the UK in 1984. She originally studied psychology, pedagogy and marketing, however, following her husband to live in the UK, she retrained in the field of make-up and special effects before joining the entertainment and film industry.

After spending twenty years in a very creative, but also fast paced and high powered environment and battling with her own health issues, Andrea finally followed her other passion, namely to support people in regaining and maintaining their physical, emotional and mental health and wellbeing. She undertook further studies in the fields of Nutrition, Wellbeing Coaching and Craniosacral Therapy, specialising in chronic conditions, in particular stress, fatigue and pain issues.

Having successfully worked in the complimentary health field for the last seventeen years Andrea believes: "The most prominent common denominator for ill health is the unrecognised multi-faceted impact of stress in our lives."

After the untimely death of her father and brother, both due to poorly managed stress, the book of The Stress Maze was born.

Andrea currently lives in Berkshire with her second husband, surrounded by nature, pets and homegrown fruit and veggies.

Mission Statement:
"Never give up, never stop learning, never be afraid to change!

Life is there to be savoured and lived"

References and Resources

Elke Wallace: References

Neuro Agility Profile Training Manual, Version 1, 2018, issued by neuro-link.net (accessible by Neuro Agility Practitioner Trainees and Practitioners only)

Chapter Eight: "The Chemistry of Survival", Evolve Your Brain by Joe Dispenza D. C., published by Health Communications Inc., Florida, U.S.A., 2007

2018 UK Study:

https://www.mentalhealth.org.uk/statistics/mental-health-statistics-stress

Percentage of illness related to stress:

https://www.ncbi.nlm.nih.gov/pmc/articles/PMC5476783/

Effects of stress on the body:

https://www.apa.org/topics/stress/body

Further recommended reading and resources:

Evolve Your Brain by Joe Dispenza D. C., published by Health Communications Inc., Florida, U.S.A., 2007

Mind UK: https://www.mind.org.uk/information-support/types-of-mental-health-problems/stress/what-is-stress/

Mental Health Foundation UK:

https://www.mentalhealth.org.uk/a-to-z/s/stress.

Nicole Price: References

Relationships: Carlson, Richard   Don't Sweat the Small Stuff – and It's All Small Stuff: Simple Ways to Keep the Little Things from Taking Over Your Life.

Published by Hyperion 1997   ISBN: 0-7868-8185-2

Ramona Stronach: Reference and resources

*Matrix Reimprinting was created by Master Karl Dawson – one of 29 EFT Masters worldwide. For more information about his work I highly recommend his book listed in the resources.

Karl Dawson, Sasha Allenby, Matrix Reimprinting using EFT, 2010

Dr Joe Dispenza, Breaking the Habit of Being Yourself, 2012

Shakti Gawain, Living in the Light, 1998

David Hamilton, How you can Heal your Body, 2008

Sir David Hawkins, The Map of Consciousness Explained, 2020

Peter Levine, In an Unspoken Voice, 2010

Bruce Lipton, The Biology of Belief, 2005

Dr Sue Morter, The Energy Codes, 2019

Jill Bolte Taylor, My stroke of Insight: a Brain Scientist's Personal Journey, 2005

Eckhart Tolle, A New Earth, 2005

Christy Whitman, The Desire Factor, 2021

Tracey Secker: References

British Journal of Psychiatry study: Dietary pattern and depressive symptoms in middle age- PMC(nit.gov)

Stress Nutrition Advice - Nutritionist Resource (nutritionist-resource.org.uk)

Effects of magnesium and vitamin B supplementation on mental health and quality of life in stressed healthy adults:Post-hoc analysis of a randomised controlled trial - Pub Med

Omega3polyunsaturated fatty acids (O3PUFA's), compared to placebo, reduced symptoms of occupational burnout and lowered morning cortisol secretion - PubMed (nah.gov)

Further reading and watching:

(PDF)Nutrient and Stress Management (research.net)

Psychological Stress, Cortisol Levels, and Maintenance of Vaginal Health - PMC (nit.gov)

Stress effects on the body (app.org)

How does Nutrition Affect Stress? - YouTube

Food Insecurity, Stress and Nutrition - YouTube

Andrea Ursula Hochgatterer: References and resources

Stress and immune function:

www.stress.org Hans Seyle The Father of Stress

Effects of stress on immune function: the good, the bad, and the beautiful Firdaus S Dhabhar 1Affiliation; Department of Psychiatry and Behavioural Sciences, Institute for Immunity,

Transplantation, and Infection, Neurosciences Institute, Cancer Institute, Stanford University, 300 Pasteur Drive, MC 5135, Stanford, CA, 94305-5135, USA, dhabhar@gmail.com PMID: 24798553 DOI: 10.1007/s12026-014-8517-0

Hormones and neurotransmitters

(Wollston 2002)

Hormones as messengers like Serotonin (95% of which are produced in the gut)influence our moods / anxiety/depression

www.Brainfacts.org Communications between the brain and the body, the vagus nerve and ups and downs in the nervous system

Gut brain axis:

www.healthlines.com, probiotics, probiotics and gut brain connection; Vagus nerve and neurotransmitters:

PUBMEDhttps://pubmed.ncbi.nlm.nih.gov/?term=Cryan%20JF &cauthor_id=31460832

The Microbiota-Gut-Brain Axis PMID: 31460832 DOI: 10.1152/physrev.00018.2018

Gut bacteria and the microbiome:

www.brainfacts.org: A gut feeling, our Microbiome and the Brain;

www.brainfacts.org: Our Microbial Minds

Mitochondria:

Psychosom Med. 2018 Feb-Mar; 80(2): 126–140.

doi: 10.1097/PSY.0000000000000544 PMCID:

PMC590165NIHMSID: NIHMS922890PMID: 29389735

Psychological Stress and Mitochondria: A Conceptual Framework

Evelyn Kessler et al A pathway coordinated by DELE1 relays mitochondrial stress to the cytosol Nature (2020). DOI: 10.1038/s41586-020-2076-4

Journal information: Nature

(Wallace, 2010). Every cell of the human body contains a variable content of 100–1000's of mitochondria, determined by energy demand of each cell type. Thus, the structure and function of When the wear and tear is strongest, we call it allostatic overload and this is what is occurring in toxic stress and (Wallace, 2010).CrossRefView Record in ScopusGoogle Scholar.

Psychological Stress and Mitochondria: A Systematic Review

Martin Picard, PhD and Bruce S. McEwen, PhD

HPA Axis:

M.E. Bowers, R. Yehuda, in Stress: Neuroendocrinology and Neurobiology, 2017

long term effect of HPA activation

Reference (in addition to linked text above):

Chrousos GP. Stress and disorders of the stress system. Nat Rev Endocrine. 2009 Jul;5(7):374-81. doi: 10.1038/nrendo.2009.106. Epub 2009 Jun 2. PMID: 19488073.

Reticular activation system:

Reticular Activating System:E.Garcia-RillUniversity of Arkansas for Medical Sciences, Little Rock, AR, USAhttps://doi.org/10.1016/B978-008045046-9.01767-8

www.study.com the function of the reticular activating system

HSPs:

Dandelion, tulips and orchids: Francesca Lionetti, Arthur Aron, Elaine N.Aron, G Leonard Burns,

Jadzia Jagiellowicz and Michael Pluess.

Aron et al 2012 PSPR

Google Scholar for sensitivity, environmental sensitivity,

The Highly Sensitive Person, Dr Elaine Aron.

Books: Thrive, the highly sensitive person, and career and thrill; the high sensation seeking highly sensitive person;

www.drtracycooper.com

EMFs

Lloyd Burrell I Electric Sense

(Ronni & Danny Wolf MD Kaplan medical centre, April 2004)

(Dr C Waldmann-Slsam, Dr. U Seger, Bamberg Germany 2005)

www.tetrawatch.net/link/links.php?id=stoiberlet

www.starwave.com/gallery

ALI Asghari, Amir Afshin Khaki, Asghar Rajabzadeh, Arash Khaki)

(REF: Breunig, Helmut"Tree Damage Caused By Mobile Phone Base Stations, an observation guide 2017)

Toxins in your home:

PubMed.gov

Antizar-Ladislao B. Environmental levels, toxicity and human exposure to tributyltin (TBT)-contaminated marine environment. a review. b_antizar@hotmail.com. Environ Int. 2008 Feb;34(2):292-308. doi: 10.1016/j.envint.2007.09.005. Epub 2007 Oct 23. PMID: 17959247.

www.organicauthority.com

www.bustle.com

www.theworldofhealth.co.uk

healthy-house.co.uk

Reading List

Your inner Physician and You: Craniosacral Therapy and SomatoEmotional Release
John E Upledger, D.O.,O.M.M. ISBN1-55643-246-1

THE POWER OF NOW: A Guide to Spiritual Enlightenment Eckhart Tolle
ISBN 978 0 340 73350 9

The Heart of Listening: A Visionary Approach to Craniosacral Work
Hugh Miln ISBN 978-1-55643-279-8

SomatoEmotional Release: Deciphering the Language of Life, John E. Upledger, D.O.,O.M.M.
ISBN 978-1-55643-412-9

When The Body Says No: The Cost of Hidden Stress, Gabor Mate,
ISBN 978-1-78504-222-5

Metaphysical Anatomy Your body is talking, are you listening? Evette Rose.
Anxiety is Really Strange, Steven Haines, ISBN 978-1-84819-389-5

www.stress.org Hans Seyle, the father of stress

Mindfulness for Health: A practical Guide to Relieving Pain, Reducing Stress and Restoring Wellbeing. Vidyamala Burch & Danny Penman

ISBN 978-0-7499-5924-1

The Insulin Factor: Could Syndrome X Be Your Problem? Antony J Haynes ISBN 0-00-716377-0

The Food Intolerance Bible; Antony J Haynes, ISBN 0-00-716382-7 Regenerate, Unlocking Your Body's Radical Resilience Through The New Biology ISBN 978-1-4019-5638-7

Aromatherapy for Healing the Spirit, Restoring Emotional and Mental Balance with Essential Oils.
Gabriel Mojay, ISBN 0-89281-887-5

Optimum Nutrition for The Mind, Patrick Holford,
ISBN 0-7499-2398-9

The Pocket guide to Polyvagal Theory, DR. Steven Porges, ISBN 978-0393707878

Polyvagal Theory in Therapy, Engaging The Rhythm Of Regulation, Deb Dana, ISBN 978-0-393-71237-7

Online Health Webinars: www.drjockers.com

Printed in Great Britain
by Amazon

13251837R00115